D1071626

Ship Management

Ship Management

A Study In
Definition
And
Measurement

by

Rodney M. Elden

Cornell Maritime Press, Inc.
Cambridge   Maryland
1962

Library of Congress Catalog Card No. 62-13791

Manufactured in the United States of America

Benjamin Franklin to his friend
Benjamin Vaughan, 1786.

" . . . and you will observe with concern how
long a useful truth may be known and exist before
it is generally received and practised upon."

Foreword

MOST available literature on the subject of ocean transportation is concerned with the myriad details of freight traffic management and the handling and documentation of cargo. The vitally important, albeit controversial, subject of ship management is usually treated in a rather summary fashion, often consisting of little more than an organization chart of some steamship company, together with short descriptions of the employees' duties. There are some good reasons for this dearth of definition.

The ubiquitous nature of ship operations breeds a climate of continuous change and infinite variations in surrounding circumstances. Thomas Thorburn, in his book *Supply and Demand of Water Transport,* published at the Stockholm School of Economics, lists ninety-five different factors, all of which influence the determination of water transport freight rates. These economic, technical and geographic factors are by their very nature interacting and dynamic and are in turn either short, medium or long term in their effect on each other and on the sum total.

It therefore becomes difficult to write on the subject of shipowning or ship management in the unequivocal sense because the circumstances and problems are so complex and so varied that most any premise can easily be shown by example and illustration to be right under one set of circumstances and wrong under another.

The author who dares to invade this area must walk an invisible tightrope stretched between dogmatism and equivocation. The only factor which shows a consistent pattern in this field is that circumstances are guaranteed to change tomorrow.

Frankly, this book is an attempt to identify and define the many real and imagined problems of ship management and, through analysis and synthesis, to establish the relative importance of each problem. A collateral and equally important aim is to determine and measure the degree of controllability inherent in each problem and thereby erect realistic objectives that reflect intelligent choice between economic alternatives.

The practical interrelationship of such sources of expense as labor, food, maintenance and insurance on board ship is probably the basic reason why these operating costs are more or less taken together and accepted in total. We suggest, however, that these ill-defined and painful totals can be factorized into clear, meaningful areas, susceptible to analysis and a major degree of cost control. This need for clear focus and useful factorization is perhaps the motivating force behind this study, and we hope that, in at least defining our grand objective, many new areas of creative thought will suggest themselves.

Some of our philosophizing into the realm of why we do certain things is intentionally provocative, and we therefore make no pretense of trying to conceal some small attempt to stimulate ideation and creative thought. Confucius said, "Show him one corner of the subject, and encourage him to find the other three." In 500 B.C., the social and scientific environment was somewhat simpler than today, and Confucius could afford to stimulate in only two dimensions. The vicious complexity of life today, however, demands that we seek an infinite number of solutions in an infinite number of dimensions.

The generation of the maximum number of solutions to a problem is not usually the province of the individual but more often is accomplished by collective genius. The man who has vision and enthusiasm might be devoid of courage and initiative. Similarly, the man with specific knowledge and the ability to synthesize might lack perseverance and constructive discontent. It is, therefore, mandatory that we seek each other's view on our common problems, and that we do so objectively. To do otherwise is to invite that lonesome and paralyzing disease known as cirrhosis of the attitude.

The subject of ship management is so vast that we have taken special pains to avoid writing a long and complex book about it. We have attempted to present the subject in a simple, straightforward way that can be understood by anyone, regardless of his experience, and in such form that it can be viewed as a whole in a single evening. To succeed in this purpose, it has been necessary to avoid the innumerable bypaths and endless variations that tempt anyone who discusses a subject on which he has given considerable thought over a long period of time.

No criticism is intended here of any profession, organization or industry, for it is clear that we do many things in the marine environment for the sake of expediency that, while undesirable on a variety of counts, are necessary to solve the problem of the moment.

We are indebted to our many friends who so willingly answered requests for information, but our greatest thanks must go to those who refused. By their very reticence, they made abundantly clear not only their affliction of mass myopia but also the need for a re-examination of their own parochial problems. This called for a certain amount of friendly pilferage, reminding us of Kipling as he wrote:

> "When Omar Smote 'is Bloomin' Lyre
> e'd 'eard Men Sing By Land and Sea
> And What 'e Thought 'e Might Require
> 'e Went An' Took——The Same As Me."

Contents

Tables

Charts

xi

Ship Management

CHAPTER ONE

The Conservator

T HE need for ocean shipping as a powerful economic tool and military weapon is so amply demonstrated in history that a repetition here would be indeed superfluous. From the time the Egyptians first ventured on the open sea to trade their grain for timber from Lebanon, the ship has been used as a tool in the form of a buoyant object to transport goods from one place to another over water, which conveniently covers 70 per cent of the earth's surface.

Genesis

While the transition from the oar-propelled barges of the Egyptians to the steamship of today has taken some 5,000 years, the ship of today is really nothing more than a complicated version of her ancient counterpart. Oars have been replaced by sails and then by steam engines; the wooden planks of the hull have been replaced by steel plates; the soldiers in the crew have been replaced by guns mounted on separate ships called a navy. But the ship is still just a buoyant object which can be propelled through the water by one means or another. The sole function of the ship is to provide a service; it does not produce anything. The only thing that the merchant ship offers, and the source from which it derives its total revenue, is the transporting of goods over the water.

Although the building of ships has always been an art and a science, ship management as such is a more or less recent development. Until about 130 years ago, a ship was merely a means to an end—a means by which the shipowner-trader or merchant earned money. Actual ship management in terms of controlled costs, budgeting and long range planning was then probably of secondary importance.

The Key to Maximum Profitability

Today much of the profitability from shipowning and operation is derived from:

1. The wise building or purchase of the ship that is best suited to the service in which she will operate.
2. The aggressive and shrewd trading instinct of the owner.
3. The skillful management of the ship at maximum annual profit consistent with reliable operation.

Item one is, of course, a function of experience, research and intelligent planning on the part of the owner and his top management. Item two is a less tangible but nevertheless an equally necessary quality. Item three concerns itself principally with the conservation of that money which is required to be spent in operating the ship. It is with this function that we are here concerned.

The Coffee House Technique

On a one-ship basis, given a certain modicum of luck, it would seem quite possible for the shipowner himself "to make his office where he hangs his hat" and to discharge the foregoing three functions all by himself with an occasional bit of advice from the experts in various fields. However, when an entire fleet of vessels is considered, together with today's maintenance, personnel and material problems, it becomes a herculean task for the owner to operate his ships singlehandedly from a coffee house.

The Involution of the Shipmaster

A ship is really operated by the master, not by a person sitting ashore, regardless of any misleading title. The person ashore responsible for maintaining *absolute minimum* operating expense is, in reality, a *conservator*. He is apparently better qualified to buy the services and materials required by the ship than the master himself; otherwise, certainly the master should be doing his own buying and conserving as in olden times and no shore staff should be required.

To be objective we should ask why, in the 1960's, the captain cannot be his own manager and conservator when we know that most ship captains were eminently qualified to do so in the 1860's. This is particularly so of the Yankee shipmaster of the clipper era whose shrewdness as a trader was legend. Although general in nature, the following reasons will probably explain this change:

1. Shipmasters of the early nineteenth century were often either part owners or full owners of their vessel and not infrequently their cargo. The incentive to conserve expenditures with such an equity in the venture cannot be duplicated.

2. Shipmasters of that era were not yet confronted with such mixed blessings as marine engineers required to operate and repair their engines—trained specialists in mechanics and steel, who intruded into the master's previously protected domain of canvas, cordage and wood. Prior to steel ships and steam engines, the master was truly the most informed person on board; ship construction, carpentry, rigging and sailmaking were skills in which he was trained and had become proficient. No specialists on board or ashore were required to tell the master what maintenance, refitting or repairs were required; he already knew better than they.

3. The progressively increasing value which has been placed on human life and the rights of seamen in the twentieth century has imposed a multitude of controls on the shipmaster which hitherto were nonexistent. These controls are international, national, local and union-made in origin and so restrict the shipmaster in the use and abuse to which he can subject his crew that in time he has become not unlike the pilot of an airplane, the user of a tool, the operator of a machine; a shadow of his former self, when he was Lord and Master of his ship and crew—shrewd trader, cunning opportunist, strict disciplinarian and absolute leader of his autonomous business venture.

The Evolution of the Conservator

In 1896 a twenty-two-year-old Italian electrical engineer traveled to England and there obtained a very famous patent, which was assigned the rather lucky number 7777. This patent covered the first wireless telegraph system and the young man's name was Guglielmo Marconi. We tend to think of Marconi's name in connection with our entertainment radio, or the saving of the lives of seamen. But, as so often happens with great inventions, the indirect effects on civilization are sometimes much greater than the direct or obvious effects.

The application in 1902 of the wireless telegraph to ship communications had some immediate and probably startling effects on the previously isolated domain of the shipmaster. Within a period of only a few years, the master's completely autonomous position was suddenly diluted by the invention of a little black box which almost instantaneously sent messages back and forth between shipowner and shipmaster.

Commander Geoffrey Lowis, in his intensely humorous collection of stories about the pre-Marconi Royal Navy (Bibliog. 1), recounts the unauthorized treasure hunt of the H.M.S. *Imperieuse*. It seems that the captain had found an old secret chart with X marking the spot, and, being an ambitious and adventurous sort of chap, he sailed off to make his fortune. The yawl *Alert* was sent to look for her but without success, and the *Imperieuse* successfully eluded detection for twelve months. Neither the Admiralty nor the Commander-in-Chief had word from her until her provisions ran out, when, failing to find the pirate hoard, she returned to the fold. The records do not indicate that the captain was ever promoted to admiral.

While Marconi's device utilized only invisible radio waves, the element of control which it created was just as positive as a steel chain. Communication times which had been reckoned in weeks and months now shrank to a few hours. Now, certainly, no major business decisions would be made at sea; many other decisions would start coming from shore. Marconi did not know it, but he probably contributed much to the development of today's ship manager or conservator.

The ship manager today is really no single person but is a team of persons. The ubiquity of our complex operations make it so. The port captain, the purchasing agent, port engineer, paymaster, claims agent —all are ship managers or, more properly, conservators. They spend 100 per cent of their time in making action decisions and in the conservation of operating expenses.

The Need for a Memory

Those who are engaged in dynamic moving operations have many problems. These are the problems of the moment, and they must be solved immediately, as the costs of debt service, wages and insurance are continually marching on while the problems of operational delays are being solved. Unexpected collisions, strikes, fires, deaths, changes in market conditions and world events all conspire to rivet the attention of the ship manager to the problem of the moment. This is as it should be. The ship manager is at once a safety valve, a complaint box, an expansion joint, a scapegoat and a convenient fireplug for any pooch that inhabits his world. He likes it. It is an exciting, moving existence in which nothing ever happens twice in exactly the same way.

But, as he is caught up in such a fast moving stream, and spends most of his time dodging the rapids, it is understandably characteristic that he has little time to spend looking astern to see where he has been or what he has done. Although man is the most adaptable mechanism known today, he has definite limitations which have now been reached. Man has many desirable abilities, but the short-term storage of large quantities of disparate pieces of information is not one of them.

Obviously, the conservator could handily use two heads—one to think about the future . . . and one to remember the past. But this cannot be. He must concentrate on the future and seek help with the past. This he does in the form of record-keeping or information re-trieval. The record of his actions over a period of time is the gauge of his performance. The better the records, the better the gauge. The quicker the retrieval, the quicker the correction. In short, today's conservator finds that to measure his performance accurately he must team up with a specialist in "information retrieval."

The ship manager today is in a unique position to increase profits by a lot of forward thinking and planning. This requires the two very important ingredients of time and thinking. Possibly no job is harder work than continuous concentration on how to outdistance your opponents. Not given sufficient time, the results then resemble a chess game in which the players are limited to ten seconds for each move.

It is understandable, then, that in the hurly-burly of his ubiquitous complex he sometimes doubts whether he is working on his most important problem, whether his shoulder is against the main wheel. This doubt results from a lack of definition of the controllable values in his various problems.

These controllable values can, of course, all be equated in dollars. If neat little fences can be erected around them, they can then be carefully watched . . . using a minimum of time. However, if the fences are not neat or tight, he will be watching a field full of sheep.

Fence Building

When time is thus released for creative thinking, the conservator can then apportion it in relation to the importance of his outstanding problems and planning. It would seem reasonable to believe that if he had six hours available and was confronted with two problems, having potential exposures of $10,000 and $2,000, that the six hours would be used in the ratio of 5 to 1. This is only common sense.

But, to be able to do this he must first know the magnitude of his exposures. He must know what his costs have been running inside each fence line and whether they are increasing or decreasing. Each of his fences must be erected around parameters which he knows can or should be controlled. If he suspects that we have been suffering an abnormal number of strandings, then a fence should be built around strandings. If he is shocked by the fact that we spend half a million dollars on paint each year, then a fence should certainly be built around paint.

Many a conservator is prone to blame the accounting profession for the fact that his fences need mending. This is the easiest thing to do, of course, but the fact is that his fences were not built by an account-ant. They were probably erected by the conservator before him who, at that time, wanted to build fences around red-headed chief engineers or captains with wooden legs. It is truly unfair to blame the accountants for something they did not do.

Cost is by Definition

In the recording of ship-operating costs, expenses are generally broken down into numerous categories so that the conservator and the shipowner will know what their money is being spent on. The practice of segregating expenses into different categories has quite possibly resulted from increasing government controls and participation in shipping activities. The operation of ships for the United States government or with subsidy has led to the general adoption of what is called the "Uniform System of Accounts for Maritime Carriers." Similar uniform systems of accounts are used in other transportation and utilities fields.

Now let us examine the generally accepted costs of operating an ocean-going ship today—the costs which the ship manager or conservator is expected to reduce, minimize or eliminate. The first thing we will encounter is the names of all the different accounts. If we agree that the accuracy of our record-keeping is really determined by words, by the definitions of our accounts, then it would seem to follow that no account can ever be more accurate than its definition.

Clarity

Some of the accounts, as they are called, appear to be quite necessary and relatively pure. Payroll Taxes is one of these. Another inviolable category is called Fuel. Fuel is fuel, and the only way it can be made into anything else is by burning it up. Similarly, nothing else is fuel, and any other expense would be rather conspicuous if it were recorded in the Fuel Account. And it is such a nice, clear definition; it would truly make a wonderful model for all other accounts.

On the other side of the coin, however, we see some rather mystifying things being done which would probably be baffling to the non-maritime mind. Food is called Subsistence, which can be defined in six different ways, only one of which seems to even resemble food. The cost of paint used to protect steel from rusting when applied by a sailor is charged to Stores, and the sailor's labor is charged to Wages. When the same paint is applied to a tank by a shore gang, it is called maintenance and charged to Other Maintenance. When the paint is applied by a shipyard, it is called Repairs and so charged.

One of the most versatile accounts we use is impressively called Maintenance and Repairs. There is good reason to believe that this is a vast, fenceless area, for only part of the paint, bricks, wire, pipe, valves and other expensive materials of maintenance are charged here; the balance is recorded as Stores. Here lies the body of much of the labor used in the maintenance of the physical ship; the rest is entered as Wages. The word "Repairs" as used in this account definition misleads us all. The common use of the word "repair," in this connection, implies that repair should be taken for granted, that it is to be expected, that it requires an expert to supervise, and that it cannot be eliminated. The truth is that the need for a repair indicates a possible design defect but more probably a maintenance failure. We understand that in nuclear engineering practice, this sort of thing is properly called a *Fault* and a correspondingly high fence built around it. In the crystal-clear words of Dr. Lester Goldsmith, "To repair *anything* is to take care of it too late."

Redefinition

Let us try to redefine the broad categories of vessel expense in the language of the people and see if it makes any more sense. For simplicity, let us assume the vessel to be a tanker or bulk carrier operating under a long-term time charter. The clear categories of expense would seem to be, in plain language:

    Labor . . . . and its Food
    Maintenance . . . . and its Materials
    Risk . . . . and its Insurance

or, we could say: Labor, Food, Maintenance, Materials and Insurance.

The Perfect Ship

Perhaps the inquisitive mind should ask, "Why must we bear these expenses at all?" We have said that a ship is just a simple, buoyant object that floats back and forth. Why can it not operate like a perfectly designed tool where the only cost is the capital cost? This is, of course, possible. The vessel would be constructed of a permanently non-corrosive material. The crew would be replaced by completely automatic control and electronic computers which would take radio orders from the owner and would report the ship's position, weather data and so forth, just as satellites do. The nuclear fuel charge would last for the full economic life of the ship and would be capitalized along with the construction cost. With the crew eliminated, negligence and human error would be eliminated. The electronic data computers would, of course, anticipate such minor remaining perils as storms, collisions, fires, rovers and pirates and would avoid them, thus

eliminating the need of insurance. And there you have it; with one
short paragraph of preliminary design, we have eliminated all operating costs.

Sound like space fiction? Not at all! Except for the somewhat casual
manner in which we have just eliminated marine perils, our perfect ship
is certainly possible. Our age is noted for its perfection of tools. Our
ideal ship will be another perfect tool.

The Base Line

Realistically, our perfect ship will not evolve from the first proto-
type. Several models will probably have to be built. But to be sure
that we set our goal at the maximum extent of our capabilities, let us set
our sights on the perfect ship—the one whose operating costs are *zero*.

This should give us a positive rather than a negative approach to
the problem of conserving money. Rather than arguing about whether
a broom should be charged to the Consumable account or the Ex-
pendable account, we will spend our time deciding whether the broom
is or is not necessary. The broom costs only 50 cents, but it requires
a man to push it. The man must be paid, fed, insured, washed and
kept warm. It almost appears that each of our principal categories of
expense have to contribute to servicing the broom.

Using a vessel whose operating costs are *zero* as a base line offers
limitless opportunities for searching analysis and self-examination.
Each dollar of expense we grudgingly approve must be fully justified by
cogent reasons, and the very existence of every custom and practice
used by our industry will be challenged, undressed, examined and then
accepted, modified or rejected. This will be no easy job and will require an objective, open mind. Let us look at what a few closed minds
did to our friends in the U.S. Navy not too long ago.

The Curse of Subjectivity

In his truly remarkable essay (Bibliog. 2) entitled "A Case Study of
Innovation," the historian Elting Morison shows us with rare clarity
the nature of the greatest barrier to change and improvement. This
is the story of how William S. Sims, a junior naval officer, overcame
the combined hostile resistance of the Navy Department to champion
the introduction of continuous aim firing to U.S. naval gunnery. Lt.
Sims' voyage to victory in this matter was not a smooth one and was
highlighted by Sims taking his personal *cause célèbre* to the President
of the United States, Theodore Roosevelt.

The many barricades which Sims had to chop through on his road
to victory can all be summed up as the inertia of "identification." The

creators of the old type of guns and sights identified themselves with their creations and thus obtained a presumed satisfaction from the thing itself, which prevented them from thinking too closely on the defects of the device. Others identified themselves with a settled way of life they had inherited or accepted with minor modification and thus found their satisfaction in attempting to maintain that way of life unchanged. Still others identified themselves as rebellious spirits, men of the insurgent cast of mind, and thus obtained a satisfaction from the act of revolt itself.

This purely personal identification with a concept, a convention or an attitude would appear to be a powerful barrier in the way of an obviously desirable change. People who have been closely identified with an activity over a long period of time instinctively tend to defend the existing order of things. We unconsciously slant facts and marshal mere dogma in support of that order. We thus not only mislead ourselves but also effectively deflect all well-meaning efforts at reform that may be tendered from outside our own group.

The End of the *Wamponoag*

Typical of the hostile barriers which Sims had to overcome were the mid-nineteenth-century admirals who "identified themselves" with sails. Congressman Herbert C. Bonner recently related a story (Bibliog. 3) that vividly illustrates this point. This was the story of a naval ship that was designed as a commerce raider during the Civil War. She was designed to prey effectively on British commerce if Britain should have joined the Confederacy. Her name was the *Wamponoag.*

As a commerce raider, her chief requirements were light armament and extreme speed. Upon completion, the shipping world was astounded when this new ship averaged 17 knots for 38 hours in a North Atlantic storm during her trial run in February, 1868. This was a notable event, since the *City of Paris* held the blue ribbon at that time for crossing the Atlantic at a maximum speed of 14 knots.

The Navy, in the early years of the transition from sail to steam, found itself in a predicament. How could this radical innovation of a ship be integrated into the established, traditional program? The account goes on to say that a board of admirals was convened to serve as a panel to decide what should be done about the *Wamponoag.*

First the experts agreed that two blades of the four-bladed propeller should be removed. Thus, the ship would perform better under sail because of reduction of drag, with the remaining two blades hiding vertically behind the stern post.

It was further agreed that four stacks on such a ship made her a disgraceful-looking craft. So the experts decided to remove two of them. The remaining two, of course, would be telescoped so the ship would look better when it was rigged and under sail. Of course, removing two of the stacks also made it necessary for them to take out half the boilers.

Then, this distinguished panel decided that it was of utmost importance that they be able to step a proper mainmast. However, a mainmast could not be stepped without the removal of the reduction gears. It was decided that this move should be made.

And, of course, by the time the experts had surveyed their own handiwork, they arrived at a decision that really the best thing to do to solve their problem would be to scrap the ship. That was the end of the *Wamponoag!* It was twenty years later, we understand, before the U.S. Navy again had a 17-knot ship.

Sans Fig Leaves

To properly examine the nature of our operating expenses it is mandatory that we keep a completely open mind. This is particularly necessary in these times of such prodigious technical and social change. What seemed to be a vitally necessary action five years ago may be totally inapplicable today.

If Archimedes, Cavendish, Edison and Einstein were asked to sit down together and give us their five-word formula for creativeness and progress, we know exactly how it would read: "Imagination and Lack of Prejudice."

Only by pretending to be "on the outside looking in" can we objectively examine practices which have evolved over hundreds of years and from thousands of sources. We may find, at the end of our analysis, that we have been doing everything perfectly. If so, our time will not have been wasted, for we will have confirmed our correctness and removed doubt. On the other hand, we may find some minor and major economies that can be effected, some useless customs eliminated, and, hopefully, we may identify those elusive criteria of smart, economical ship operation which have heretofore escaped definition.

CHAPTER TWO

Labor

A T THE 1948 Safety of Life at Sea Convention in London, each signatory nation agreed (Part V, Regulation 13) to ensure that, "from the point of view of safety of life at sea, all [of its] ships shall be sufficiently and efficiently manned." In the translation, each maritime nation agrees to the principle that "a vessel shall not be navigated unless it has in its service and on board a sufficient complement of officers and crew as are necessary for safe navigation." The question of how many are "sufficient" necessarily remains vague unless the word "safe" can be defined.

Sufficient or Efficient

United States law identifies the Coast Guard as the agency to judge the minimum number of men necessary for actual safe navigation. Norwegian law appears to go the limit and concerns itself with the vessel's total manning, including all the unskilled persons having nothing to do with safe navigation.

Included in United States maritime law are such restrictions as limiting a seaman's work to eight hours a day, the granting of holidays to seamen when a vessel is in port, and restrictions against shipping seamen to work alternately in the boiler room and on deck. Additional restrictions imposed by American maritime unions usually prohibit crew members standing watch from performing even routine maintenance work while on watch.

It is no secret that any shipowner would like to run his ships with smaller crews or no crews at all. This economic fundamental applies to any employer or business; even to the military establishment. The crew member who is not a decision maker is a definite burden, and on nuclear submarines he even limits the endurance of the venture by inconsiderately breathing as much oxygen as his captain.

Substantial changes in the present scheme of things would seem to reduce costs in some directions and increase them in others. Let us look at some of the questions which this thought provokes:

What does the crew actually do on board and why?

Is the size of crews generally used too large or too small?

Does the presence of officers and crew actually dilute the reliability of proven automatic equipment and instrumentation through human errors in judgment?

What are the elements of cost control in the total cost of maintaining a ship's crew?

In seeking the answers to these questions, let us first examine the nature of our labor force.

The Seaman

In 1939, Professor Herbert L. Seward (Bibliog. 4) succinctly clarified some of the popular misconceptions about the relationship of a seaman to his employer and his ship. The Professor's rare insight and observations are still applicable today.

Sea labor unions began to organize at a time when the shipowners had very little idea of the importance of good relations between employer and employee. The unions fought for better and fairer conditions, for increased wages and for personal freedom as citizens or resident aliens. To Andrew Furuseth, leader of the marine labor movement, a seaman was a serf when he should be a free man—as free as anyone else who earned his living by the sweat of his brow—as free as anyone anywhere. If there is any justification for considering the seaman in a certain sense as a serf, it can only be because there the worker must live on his job. The company has to furnish him living accommodations as part of his contract. For this there is very little parallel on land except in construction or lumber camps or under like frontier conditions.

On the old sailing ship the accommodations and food were primitive. With the rise of modern powered vessels and the complete change in ship construction, crew quarters and fare did not receive as much attention as did those of the passengers. When labor unions began to express themselves for needed improvements, they were bitterly opposed by many shipowners, of whom it might be said, in the incomparable words of Harold Scarborough: "Each concession was made, with remarkable nicety, just when it no longer could be deferred."

Improved Conditions

Reiterated propaganda has painted the shipowner as having kept the seaman in serfdom until comparatively recently. It insists that by grinding down his labor in the past he merited whatever happens to him now. It paints him as opposing any change in conditions at sea, and ascribes all improvement as due solely to the militant tactics of organized labor.

The fact is that conditions at sea have been changing in the same manner and for the same reasons that living conditions ashore have changed. It is true that the crew's quarters on board ship are cramped; so are the passenger staterooms. Problems of naval architecture demand space economies afloat which are not necessary ashore. Ship accommodations, lighting and heating have improved as improvements became available.

Air conditioning, movies, private cabins and even swimming pools for the crew can be found on many ships built since 1950. Probably many of the current embellishments which go beyond any national or union requirements have developed in an effort to attract better men to the sea and to keep them there.

Life on the Bounding Main

The increasing difficulty of attracting men to a sea life is a fact, but with it we often take for granted that men are less keen to go to sea now than they were a couple of generations ago. There are many people who agree with C. C. Pounder (Bibliog. 5), who doubts that men were ever keen to go to sea—exceptions apart—but that they had to do so out of sheer economic necessity. Certainly youngsters now go to sea less from what are aptly called escape motives, and they probably want to see the world as much as ever, but it is undeniable that opportunities for employment and advancement ashore were certainly much more limited fifty years ago. For all practical purposes, there were no automobiles, movies, electric lights or airplanes. Leisure was only for the rich. There was no billion-dollar pleasure industry manufacturing water skis, hula hoops, fishing poles, golf clubs or swimming pools. On farms there were men and horses. In the cities there were horse-drawn vehicles. When the first oil well was brought in at Titusville, Pennsylvania, in 1859, 96 per cent of all hard labor was performed by men and only 4 per cent by machines. Today, the figures are exactly reversed.

Opportunity Ashore

In our time, one of the most difficult things to do is to maintain a proper sense of proportion in our constantly changing world. Somehow or other we have become accustomed to change, but we cannot always keep in mind the *rate* at which change itself is accelerating. Today, the automobile, airplane, petroleum and defense industries, to mention only a few, absorb workers by the millions, and at many places in the complex pattern of it all there are openings for men trained at sea, especially engineers. This probably accounts for marine engineers being today the officers in shortest supply.

There is opportunity ashore, however, for everyone. Sailors can find work as painters and riggers, and firemen can work in powerhouses. Stewards and waiters can return to the hotels whence they came. We know captains who have come ashore to take jobs as pilots, stevedoring superintendents and surveyors. Marine engineers can work in shipyards or almost anywhere in the industrial complex.

If seamen, particularly engineers, are not now interested in seagoing as a career and if this outlook is likely to continue, it may be a waste of time to try to change the trend. The present living conditions on board ship, the rates of pay, working conditions, lengthy vacations and other benefits are so good that, if men will not remain at sea, the fact must be taken as indicating a definite social change.

Re-evaluation Indicated

The ultimate result of present trends should logically lead to a re-examination of the entire ship-manning question. Just because large crews have traditionally been used is no reason to consider them necessary today. Collaterally, just because good seamen are hard to find is no reason in itself to assume that automation, in the usual sense of the word, will solve the problem.

In this age of guided missiles and orbiting satellites the questions often arise, "Why have a commander or a crew at all? Why not make everything automatic?" The answer is that man is the only mechanism we know that is capable of making decisions on the spot. Psychologists tell us that man's brain contains something in the order of ten to the seventeenth power neuron, which might be likened to "Flip Flops" in a computer. When we hear that maintenance costs of much electronic computing equipment often run to ten times the capital cost, our imagination is unable to envision the shape of a computer that might replace man's maintenance-free brain.

On Men and Machines

In any evaluation of the man-machine combination, perhaps the most important step is the determination of the proper division of tasks between the man and the machine. This division process demands an honest and rigorous appraisal of the human operator's capabilities. In this context it must be remembered that suitable instrumentation, information displays and fail-safe devices are all machines. Since the quality of a human operator's decision-making ability is directly linked with the information presented to him, it is imperative that these task divisions be determined with extreme accuracy. Any errors at this point will seriously influence the demands placed on other elements of the man-machine system. This fact cannot be overemphasized.

While the following list is far from complete and is general rather than specific, it illustrates some of the fundamentals that are ignored when we arbitrarily assign this or that function to the second mate or install some new gadget through custom or whim.

CHARACTERISTIC	MAN	MACHINE
Has perceptual constancy	Yes	No
Ability to predict and anticipate	Yes	No
Ability to make decisions and re-program	Yes	No
Ability to salvage man-machine under conditions of machine failure	Yes	No
Ability to change mental set or goal orientation at will	Yes	No
Ability to reason inductively	Yes	No
Freedom from fatigue	No	Yes
Ability to resist boredom and inattention to routine tasks	No	Yes
Unlimited power output	No	Yes
Ability to monitor well	No	Yes
Can be changed from present form	No	Yes
Ability to erase previous memory traces	No	Yes
Ability to store large amounts of information on short-term basis	No	Yes
Is a good integrator of disparate pieces of information	No	Yes

A fundamental mistake which is often made in the man-machine relationship is neglecting to appreciate over-all system efficiency. It is basic that in any man-machine system, the over-all efficiency is a function of the efficiency of the man times the efficiency of the machine.

$$\text{Over-all System Efficiency} = \text{Efficiency of Man} \times \text{Efficiency of Machine}$$

If either of these is low, the product can never be higher than the lowest value. It is therefore extremely important to achieve a balanced man-machine system.

Instrumentation Yesterday

Only a score of years ago, in most ships a few pressure gauges and thermometers were the only instruments to be found in the ship's engine room. Even the steam temperature, if anyone was interested, was determined from the pressure. The forerunners of instrumentation were the visual cues and senses of the human watchkeepers.

The temperature of bearings and moving parts were determined by touch and smell. Governors and safety devices, if any, were simple mechanical things out in plain sight for the eyes to see. Boiler performance was, to no small degree, measured by the number of complaints from the bridge about smoke. A leaking ammonia pipe announced itself to the world by burning the eyes and nose of the oiler as he went aft to feel the steering engine. Instrumentation was by the human senses—sight, sound, smell and touch.

Instrumentation Today

With the unprecedented technological advances triggered by World War II, the steamship of today either has, or has available to it, instruments to measure, record and announce almost any phenomenon which might exist or be expected. Temperatures, pressures, humidity, speeds, quantities, qualities can all be measured, recorded and controlled within limiting values, most of them automatically.

In fact, many ships of today might be considered to be over-instrumented, but underprotected, considering the number of crew being used. Possibly nothing is more dangerous, no stage better set for tragedy, than the person who does not believe his instruments. Such situations are common and are reminiscent of Dr. Goldsmith's story of the old German who sat up in bed holding an alarm clock and said, "If this damn thing don't soon go off, I'll miss my train."

We are reminded of a recent case in which failure to believe visual and audible alarms resulted in failure of a main engine lubrication system with resulting damage amounting to $60,000. Through simple maloperation, the wrong valve was closed in changing over lubricating oil coolers. The alarms immediately went into action, having been patiently waiting for two years, awake 24 hours a day, to demonstrate their loyalty and reliability. Three successive sets of audible and visual alarms went off, indicating the progressively deteriorating conditions in three separate parts of the lubrication system. This constituted six separate signals that were ignored by two men. Actually, they did respond to the least important alarm signal but doubted its veracity. While wasting their time manually checking the authenticity of this one signal, the engine ran out of oil and was severely damaged. The single fail-safe protective mechanism, the low oil trip, did not function. These wrong actions were not made intentionally, but were the result of inadequate training coupled with incomplete testing and skimpy protection. The same ingredients can be found in the true history of many casualties.

As Dr. Goldsmith so clearly observed in 1947, "The most amazing thing about 'lack of precautions' is the fact that a ship goes away from home leaving its supervision behind. It seems strange that those operating men who go to sea, who probably are the most resourceful mechanical men we have, who, regardless of their troubles, always have ingenuity enough to find means to bring them home, are sent to sea without the aid and protection of instruments that we all use ashore where supervision is constantly available. There is good reason to believe that the fundamental precaution to be taken in connection with the modern marine steam power plant is to see to it that the plant is protected with every modern device to ensure that it will operate in safety and will bring home machine-made records to prove it."

The Myth of Safe Navigation

Safety is defined as "freedom from danger or hazard" and "the quality of being devoid of whatever exposes one to danger or harm." Considering that rocks, wind, water, fire, ignorance, fear and a host of other factors contribute to exposing one to danger or harm, then it becomes rather difficult to equate safe navigation with the number of officers and crew required to be on board.

As would be expected in a sea of conflicting interests, opinion is divided on the effectiveness of different measures to promote maritime safety. Some feel certain that only rigid legislation can effectively regulate ships and those who operate them. Some are equally certain that safety can be achieved only through proper training and education. Others equivocate that a utopian mixture of legislation, enforcement and education is required to obtain the best results.

Amidst this tangle of hypotheses, arguments, opinions and theories, three things stand out as basic:

1. Relatively speaking, it is much easier to legislate than it is to educate. Legislation is the path of least resistance.

2. Ships and lives are seldom lost from a numerical lack of manpower. More often the root cause is a lack of trained manpower or lack of brainpower.

3. A close examination of the true cause of any casualty will almost invariably disclose that some basic fundamental was unknown or was ignored.

As one nation's current view, the minimum number of officers and crew considered necessary for the safe navigation of medium- and large-sized tankers by the U.S. Coast Guard is shown following:

1 Master	1 Chief Engineer
3 Mates	3 Assistant Engineers
1 Radio Operator	3 Oilers
9 Seamen	3 Firemen
──	──
14	10

The ten men required in the engine department of this vessel are in reality replacements for a considerably greater number of men that were required on the sailing vessel. Today's industrial civilization did not really commence to grow up until men learned how to convert coal's energy into mechanical work with the help of water as steam.

Increasingly, we see in the press speculation of the unmanned ship of the future. A British firm has completed a design study of a 28,000-ton self-discharging nuclear submarine ore carrier. Plans call for a very small crew to begin with, and the starry-eyed predict entirely unmanned operation with future improvements in automation. A new type of compact internal combustion engine has just been developed which is said to have only two moving parts. Even at its present limit of 700 horsepower, such a unit would seem admirably suited to a multi-engined, bridge-controlled ship, with all engine maintenance done ashore on an exchange basis.

Fossil fuels may or may not be replaced by nuclear energy or something else in the future, but at present steam turbines and diesel engines are still of primary importance for the generation of power and are likely to remain so for a long time. One need not be equipped with a built-in negative reflex to realize some of the extremely complex human, operating and maintenance problems that will attend the use of nuclear power, as we know it, in merchant ships. It is worth remembering that we already have an abundance of problems, especially in the area of maintenance, that remain unsolved even on conventional ships.

The nuclear merchant ship as we know it today is certainly not complicated in the eyes of the designers. It does, however, present certain operating problems that are not very romantic to contemplate. Not the least of these will be the chief engineer who thinks the main purpose of a ship is to carry his engines around and perhaps a little cargo if it is not too inconvenient.

However, all of the shipmasters who have been having trouble with their chief engineers since the engineers became licensed officers in 1852 were probably overjoyed 107 years later when the AEC unveiled their SNAP-3 generator or System of Nuclear Auxiliary Power. In the SNAP generator, produced by the Martin Company, heat generated by the radioactive decay of Polonium-210 is converted directly into electrical energy by a series of thermocouples. This device appears to be sealed and it contains no moving parts, and therefore needs no maintenance or supervision during operation.

Additionally, General Electric, Westinghouse, Allis Chalmers and others are currently involved in urgent research to develop the most efficient method of making the direct transition from heat to electrical energy. The four most promising systems are reported to be fuel cells and thermoelectric, thermionic and MHD generators. Allis Chalmers has already demonstrated its propane gas fuel cell running a tractor. In Great Britain the Carbox fuel cell is expected to go to work propelling delivery trucks and city buses in a few years.

Conceivably, these types of heat converters could be used to power simple, sealed electric motor drive which could be bridge-controlled in a manner of almost schoolboy simplicity. With suitable instrumentation and recording apparatus plus automatic bilge pumps and other reliable hardware, the engine crew of the future can be drastically reduced and possibly eliminated. Needless to say, there will be some who will object that, in eliminating the engine crew, there will be no one left for the highly skilled task of cleaning the bilge pump strainer. The answer to this is that with no crew in the engine room, there will be nobody to throw cigarettes, pocket combs and old magazines into the bilges and block up the strainer.

There is good reason to believe that package propulsion units, capable of converting heat directly to electrical energy, will alleviate the shortage of engineers by eliminating the demand.

Time Study

In an attempt to take a quantitative look at how a crew spends its time at sea and in port, we asked a trained observer to make a detailed time study of the crew's activities over the course of a 16-day round voyage. The condensed results of this time study, shown in Table 1, are findings of fact on one vessel and nothing more. It is realized that work patterns will vary between different owners, trades and ships.

TABLE 1. TIME STUDY

35,000 DWT Bulk Carrier

South America to
North of Hatteras Ports

48-MAN CREW

WORK CATEGORY	AT SEA		IN PORT	
	HOURS	%	HOURS	%
Navigating and Engine Watches	146		86	
Port Watches, Deck	0		54	
Anchoring, Docking, Shifting	0		39	
Routine, Soundings, Misc.	4		6	
Payrolls, Requisitions, etc.	3		12	
Safety, Fire Protection	1		1	
	154	39	198	45
Maintenance, Exposed Areas	65		63	
Maintenance, Protected Areas	36		14	
Repairs	53		62	
	154	39	139	31
Food Handling, Cooking	17		17	
Food Serving	9		11	
Maintenance of Galley, Messrooms	19		14	
Maintenance of Quarters, Passageways	25		25	
Non-daily Cleaning Chores, Laundry	11		34	
Stores Handling	2		7	
	83	22	108	24
Daily Totals	391		445	

The significant findings of this time study would seem to be that at sea the total man-hours are used on the following functions:

Safe navigation and keeping watch	39%
Maintenance	39%
Feeding and cleaning quarters	22%

The pattern in port seems to change only slightly, reflecting the use of 8 per cent of the man-hours in mooring, cargo watching and stores handling, all at the expense of maintenance.

Wage Breakdown

Table 2 shows a breakdown of a crew's total wages according to the crew's three principal activity functions. The wage scale approximates that in effect on medium-sized cargo vessels of North European registry during 1961. The individual rates of compensation are of interest only to the seamen, as generally the pay scales of the European maritime countries are within 5 or 10 per cent of one another.

TABLE 2.   WAGE BREAKDOWN BY GROUPS
Wages and Food Cost Related to Service Performed

	MONTHLY BASE WAGES	25%	FOOD	TOTAL	%
Keeping Watch					
Master, 3 Mates, Radio Operator, 5 Able Seamen	2510	627	797	3934	32
Chief, 3 Watch Engineers, 3 Firemen, 3 Oilers	2245	561	797	3603	29.5
				7537	61.5
Maintenance					
Bosun, Carpenter, 2 Able Seamen, 3 Ordinary Seamen, 3 Boys	760	190	797	1747	14.5
1st Engineer, 3 Jr. Engineers, Electrician, Donkeyman, Storekeeper, 2 Wipers, 1 Boy	1730	434	797	2961	24
				4708	38.5
Feeding					
Steward, 2 Cooks, Galleyman, 3 Messmen, 1 Boy	1015	253			
Total (48 Men)	$8,260	$2,065		$12,245	

NOTE: 25% includes average overtime and pro rata vacation. Food charged to each group at rate of $1.33 per man-day and weighted with ¼ of stewards department wages plus their food.

In this analysis, each of the four groups of ten men performing the principal functions has been charged with the exact total wages and all other compensation due their particular ratings, plus one-quarter of the out-of-pocket cost of maintaining the feeding establishment. This is based on the premise that, if the men were not present on the vessel, it would not be necessary to feed them.

Table 2 appears to demonstrate that the principal categories of activity create the following total wage and food costs:

		Monthly	Annually
Keeping watch	61.5%	7,537	90,444
Maintenance	38.5%	4,708	56,496
	100%	$12,245	$146,940

Overtime Analysis

Table 3 illustrates the extreme variations in the expenditure of overtime that can occur between similar vessels in the same trade. The significant point in the analysis seems to be the fact that the overtime expended by the engine departments of the five vessels studied is relatively stable, while the amount of overtime expended by the deck and steward's departments is rather erratic, varying by as much as 120 per cent between vessels.

TABLE 3.   AVERAGE MONTHLY OVERTIME IN DOLLARS

Twelve-Month Period

VESSEL	A	B	C	D	E	VARIATION
Deck	946	550	764	749	646	72%
Engine	570	460	515	660	433	52%
Steward's	260	165	172	276	125	120%
Total	1776	1175	1451	1685	1204	51%

Minimum Requirements for Safe Navigation

Table 4 describes four different minimum manning schemes as compared with the average manning scale of about 48 men which is used by most maritime countries in practice. The Norwegian and United States manning scales are the actual minimum requirements of those countries. For comparison, all five manning scales have been priced at wage rates that represent current average wages of North European seamen.

The column entitled "Bare Minimum Requirements" attempts to establish a fundamental navigating base line. This scale allows only six officers and six men, but it is felt that the ship could navigate in comparative safety with this number of men, provided that no emergencies or unusual circumstances arose and obviously that no maintenance was accomplished. It goes without saying that these twelve men would have to cook and shift for themselves while off watch. Similarly, it is apparent that this manning scale would probably violate The International Safety of Life at Sea Convention (SOLASC).

The column entitled "Practical Minimum Requirements" is an attempt to create a manning scale that would, for all practical purposes, satisfy the legal requirements of SOLASC and would also satisfy the practical requirements of safe navigation to fully protect the economic aspects of the venture. It will be noted that the same number of men are available for navigation and watch duties as are presently used in these functions even with a 48-man crew (see Table 2).

The use of the "Practical" Manning Scale would involve the following requirements:

a. The cook and mess boy would be qualified as seamen and able to act as such in emergencies.
b. The radio operator would be qualified as an electrician.
c. One able seaman would act as bosun/storekeeper and spend most of his time maintaining gear.
d. The mess boy would assist the cook, clean officers' rooms and be a general handy man.
e. The one oiler would not stand watch but would be responsible for all oiling and greasing on a systematic schedule.
f. The two donkeymen would be Jacks-of-all-trades working for the chief engineer but also available to help the mate and to handle lines.

The workability of the "Practical" Manning Scale would be enhanced by elements such as the following:

a. Propulsion machinery, boilers and auxiliaries would be of top quality and would be furnished by a single manufacturer.
b. All accommodations and navigating facilities would be of reasonable size to minimize maintenance and would be grouped together in one location, preferably aft.
c. The master's cabin would be adjacent to the 360° pilot house.
d. The chief engineer's cabin would be adjacent to a central control and observation room, equipped with remote gauges, thermometers, recorders and duplicates of all alarms and safety trips in the machinery spaces or, alternatively, closed circuit television.
e. All remote instruments would be of top quality manufacture, and provisions for testing and calibration would be present.
f. An engine-room elevator would be provided to transport stores and parts and to reduce the fatigue created by climbing ladders.

g. The layout of machinery for ease of operation and accessibility would be the subject of an intensive study before construction, with models and mock-ups to be built and rebuilt until ideal functional configuration is reached.

h. The auxiliary diesel generator would be a package unit capable of handling the entire auxiliary load.

i. All steel surfaces, interior and exterior, subject to corrosion would be specially treated with the most efficient coatings available.

j. Deck auxiliaries would be electric, with underdeck motors.

TABLE 4. MINIMUM MANNING SCALES—35,000 DWT VESSEL

RATING	AVERAGE MANNING	MINIMUM REQUIREMENTS			
		NORWAY	U.S.	BARE	PRACTICAL
Master	1	1	1	1	1
Mates	3	3	3	2	3
Rad. Opr.	1	1	1		1
Bosun/Carp.	2	1			
Able Seamen	7	6	6	3	5
Ord. Seamen	3	4	3		
Boys	3	4			
	20	20	14	6	10
Chief Engr.	1	1	1	1	1
Ass't Engrs.	4	2	3	2	3
Jr. Engrs.	3	1			
Firemen	3	4	3	3	3
Oilers	3	2	3		1
Donkeymen	2	3			2
Electrician	1	1			
Boys	3	2			
	20	16	10	6	10
Steward	1	1			
Cooks	2	2			1
Mess Boys	5	3			1
	8	6	0	0	2
Number	48	42	24	12	22
Monthly Wages and Overtime	$10,325	8619	6413	4175	6413

Conclusions and Recommendations

A basic crew of about 20 trained men is required for the safe navigation and operating function of today's ocean-going vessel of medium size. This is recognized in all maritime nations by international agreement for the following two principal reasons:

1. The size of modern ships, the type and layout of machinery and equipment in use, and the lack of fully reliable automation, instrumentation and functional arrangement require the services of about six men on continuous duty to manually watch, monitor, adjust and otherwise control the ship to see that it performs in a reasonably efficient and safe manner.
2. The eight-hour day, not likely to be increased, and the extreme length of sea voyages as compared with other means of transport, require, in effect, that a vessel carry three full watch crews.

The additional 20 to 35 crewmen used on most merchant ships today are engaged in the maintenance function and the feeding function. Many of the 20 or more special ratings in use for seamen are unnecessary and carry a connotation of an indispensable specialist, thus prejudicing their elimination.

Nevertheless, current manning scales in use should be re-evaluated, as some immediate reductions are possible with no sacrifice in efficiency or safety. Additionally, further detailed time studies on different types of vessels would be most beneficial. Such studies should be planned by persons expert in such analysis and should reveal areas of work adaptable to automation and remote control. All time spent on the maintenance function in each of the principal cause categories should be highlighted by the study.

Although only about 39 per cent of a crew's time is spent in navigating and keeping watch, the cost of these required activities consumes 61.5 per cent of the labor dollar because these duties are performed by the skilled, higher paid personnel. Maintenance is accomplished by the expenditure of about 39 per cent of the crew's time at a cost of about 39 per cent of the labor dollar.

Base wages are controllable only through selection of the proper manning scale for each individual vessel. Current manning scales in use could be reduced up to 50 or 60 per cent in number and 40 per cent in cost depending on the vessel's: excellence of design; quality of machinery and equipment; quality of workmanship in initial construction; port time available for maintenance; quality of over-all corrosion control; quality of continuous machinery maintenance; quality of remaining crew; excellence of administration.

Overtime is a partially controllable cost. It falls into the main categories of "operational" and "maintenance" overtime and thence into division by departments. Given a free hand, different ships and different department heads will expend widely varying amounts of overtime with widely varying results.

The cost of maintenance accomplished by the crew is much higher than appears on the surface. Not only the wages of the maintenance personnel must be considered, but also all of the many supporting costs related to these persons' "dependent" status on board. In addition to this, all costs of maintenance materials used must be considered. This includes tens of thousands of dollars worth of costly paint and coatings.

The cost of a ship's crew is often erroneously equated with the actual cash paid to the crew. In calculating the true total cost, all of the following must be considered:

Base wages	Laundry service
Overtime pay	Dishes, cutlery, etc.
All fringe benefits	Linen, soap, matches, etc.
Days off while employed	Capital cost of living quarters
Vacation pay	Maintenance of quarters
Cost of food	Fuel used in cooking
Cost of preparing food	Medical costs
Fuel for heating and cooling	Repatriation costs
Capital cost of lifesaving gear	Medical claims costs
Maintenance of lifesaving gear	Cost of maintaining morale

There are millions of dollars to be saved directly and indirectly in improving and reducing the maintenance function. But it is doubtful that substantial savings can be made in the operating function until the direct transition from heat to electrical energy becomes practical in the required power range.

A happy, interested, well-trained crew of 24 men would do a much better job of safe navigation, operation, damage control and administration than a group of 48 people merely assembled at random. Good officers and seamen, like good doctors or anything else, are made, not born. Adequate training is the quickest and least expensive way to improve personnel quality. In any event, every effort should be made to obtain and keep the best officers available, particularly the four senior officers.

Due to the advent of radio communications, today's shipmaster has become an administrator of routine as compared to his nineteenth-century "Yankee Trader" counterpart. This can be remedied by giving shipmasters more business responsibility so that they will feel responsible for the economic success of the venture as well as the mechanical success.

Crew morale on most merchant ships is relatively low. Prolonged absence from home, family and friends produces mental health problems or what has been termed "Seafarer's Depression" by the World Health Organization of the United Nations. With morale low, morals often seek a similar level. With untold sources of morale building available today, the sailor's interest during his idle time is still allowed to gravitate to rum, tobacco, and one other thing, just as it has for centuries.

Sailors are people, just like everyone else. They have feelings, emotions, hopes, families, ambitions, fears and prejudices. At the same time, they have a tremendous capacity for courage, loyalty, hardship, work and ingenuity that is unmatched in most places ashore. Their latent capacities are in most cases only partially tapped.

Every opportunity should be seized to improve crew morale. Dozens of inexpensive means exist which will provide tenfold returns:

Amusement movies	Seniority pay
Training movies	Safety competition
Safety movies	Good mail service
Television	Ship's newspaper
Supervised library service	Promotion from within

The alternative is to have crews who feel like trapped animals and give service in kind.

CHAPTER THREE

Food

For the immediate future it will probably be necessary to carry some crew members on seagoing ships—perhaps not the 48 men which are now carried on most ships, but at least the 24 men who are presently required by international agreement or by individual national regulations for the safe navigation of the vessel.

An Obligation

As stated before, the seaman must live on his job, and, traditionally, under such conditions the owner has inherited an obligation to feed him. Certainly, in some small coasting vessels or trawlers the seamen still furnish their own food, but it will probably be found that the wages of such seamen reflect this.

It is not uncommon in the shipping industry to hear remarks about a crew that is grumbling about its food. This usually seems to be mentioned in a rather humorous way, with the qualification that sailors are always grumbling about something and it might as well be the food. Others like to use the well-worn folklore that it is a healthy sign when the men are grumbling about the food, for when they stop grumbling there is really something wrong.

Alternatively, there are some who believe that there is probably no one thing more important to the working man than his food. There would seem to be some merit in this argument. Even to the Chinese coolie who has only two earthly possessions—his food and his family—the food is the only thing he cannot do without. Some rather eminent medical and psychological authorities have suggested that a happy digestive system is by far the most important single factor to man's general health and well-being. Possibly, shipowners are overlooking a tremendous untapped source of energy, alertness, loyalty and hard work for which they have been paying, but not necessarily getting.

Ship managers like to discuss their cost of feeding. Those who can feed each man for $1.20 a day are rather happy about it, while those who are paying $1.40 wonder how they can reduce their costs. Never do we hear them discussing what they are really getting for their $1.20 a day. It is possible that the lower cost ship may be feeding the men better and that the higher cost ship may be wasting food. This, however, is pure speculation, as the exact reverse could be true.

Sans Taste, Sans Everything

For those who are interested in locating the absolute minimum base line, we have found that it is theoretically possible to feed a man for 21 cents a day. Recently (Bibliog. 6), a research group at Brown University fed this problem to an IBM electronic computer. The computer, of course, ignored variety and all of life's spices, but did consider man's basic requirements for certain minimum quantities of protein, vitamins, etc. On completion of its calculations, the computer announced that only four foods are needed to sustain human life. Sailors will be very unhappy to learn that these four foods are lard, beef liver, orange juice and soybean meal.

With less culinary than mathematical skill, the research team did their best to make these ingredients into a palatable meal. Apparently they failed, for it is reported that even the laboratory dog refused the *plat du jour*. The conclusion of the researchers was that a computer could live cheaper than a human because it has no taste buds.

Not Enough Cooks Spoil the Broth

Those of us who board ships frequently see some strangely different food being served. On some ships the food is interesting, varied and tasty, yet simple. On other ships it seems to be just food . . . the crew eat it but never ask for second helpings or compliment the cook. On others it often seems like someone went out of his way to make the food taste flat, tough or indigestible. Why is there such a difference?

There is some reason to believe that such a variance between ships, furnished with the same food supplies, lies in the ability of the chief steward and the chief cook. Almost invariably we will find that the "good feeding" ship has a steward and cook who are experienced, get along together, and are happy with their jobs. They like what they are doing. It is not surprising to find that the successful stewards and cooks have had some good hotel experience and that some have even learned their trade in Switzerland.

On the other hand, if we look closely at the cooks and stewards who manage to scrape by, we will find a complete lack of training in the art of planned, economical, interesting cooking. The missing ingredient in the lobscouse seems to be a generous pinch of training.

Russian Roulette, Supermarket Style

Propaganda of the U.S. Department of Health, Education and Welfare tells us that Americans are the best fed people in the world. This, of course, is only because they are the most luxuriously fed people and not because of planning or design. Myriad advertisements, illustrated in Kodacolor, hawk the taste-tempting advantages of dumping a can of shrimps into a pan of tomato soup. We are constantly being fed the illusion that, with so many pretty things to eat, we must be getting a balanced diet and the ingredients must contain the required nutrients automatically. The implication is that, by merely grabbing some cans off the shelf or by not eating the same thing two nights in a row, we will automatically expose ourselves to a balanced diet, rich in the necessary nutrients. This is a sort of Russian roulette restaurant, in which sooner or later the firing pin is supposed to hit the right vitamin.

What is Required?

No one would deny the desirability of good health. Who would say that he does not want clear eyes and skin, sound teeth, firm muscle tone, an alert expression and a general feeling of well-being? We are told that to enjoy continued good health we must eat seven basic types of food:

Green and yellow vegetables	Milk and milk products
Oranges, tomatoes, grapefruit, etc.	Meat, poultry, fish or eggs
Potatoes and other vegetables and fruits	Bread, flour or cereal
Butter or fortified margarine	

The purpose of these foods is to supply the necessary protein, fats, carbohydrates, minerals and vitamins. It would almost seem impossible that all of the required nutrients could be obtained in the necessary amounts without quality control in addition to planned nutrition. For example, consider the simple carrot, a member of the parsley family, whose roots we eat as a vegetable. Identical-looking carrots have been shown to have an iodine content as high as 1000 ppm and as low as 20 ppm. If the inferior carrots were priced at 9¢ per pound, then we could pay as high as $4.50 per pound for the superior carrots and get the same value.

There is some indication here that the fully balanced diet could have some weak spots and also that it is probably the most expensive way to obtain all the necessary nutrients.

Vitamins Discovered at Sea

Interestingly enough, the problem of vitamin deficiency seems to have been discovered at sea. In 1747, Dr. James Lind of the British Navy discovered Vitamin C in his experiments with scurvy. In 1882, Dr. Takaki, of the Imperial Japanese Navy discovered Vitamin B_1 in the husks of polished rice during his search for the cause of beri-beri. Of course, the specific vitamins were not identified and named at that time, but their existence was confirmed and proven.

Sailors have always been noted for their understandable and magnetic attraction to alcohol. Whether consumed aboard or ashore, alcohol is seldom used by the sailor as a simple social device or as an *apéritif*. More often than not it is being used as an escape to a happy, jolly world of fantasy that cannot be found on board ship. When a sailor is drinking he either does not have the money left for food or is not hungry anyway. When this process goes on for several days followed by perhaps a week of post-alcoholic gastritis with very limited food intake, it can readily be seen that the sailor's body is sometimes literally starved for periods of ten days or more. When no food is being eaten, then obviously none of the required nutrients are being supplied.

Contrary to popular belief, there is still some hard work done on ships today such as hauling lines, lifting stores, painting and pulling chain-falls. These activities are not adventures of the mind but are just plain hard work that is usually performed under conditions of exposure. This physical work is accomplished at the expense of burning carbohydrates as fuel. The more fuel that is burned, the more Vitamin B_1 is required to act as a catalyst in the oxidation process.

According to Dr. Henry Borsook, Professor of Biochemistry at the California Institute of Technology, it is possible, for five cents, to synthesize the amount of Vitamin A in seven pounds of butter or the Vitamin B in more than 100 pounds of wheat or the Vitamin C in four quarts of orange juice. Dr. Borsook comes forward with a refreshing observation when he states, "The time has come when nutrition had best end its colonial status relation to agriculture. Official agriculture, that is political and bureaucratic agriculture, is concerned primarily with the farmer's income and not primarily with the people's nutrition."

We are not suggesting that today's seamen are alcoholics or that they are about to drop from malnutrition or beri-beri. Their diet is probably better than it has ever been. There is reason to believe, however, that even if seamen's nutrition were a planned procedure, which it is not, there would still exist the possibility of vitamin and mineral deficiency in their diet. This is probably the only area in the field of ship management, or any other business, where the problem might be solved by swallowing a capsule costing a few pennies.

Food Costs of Different Companies

Table 5 shows the comparative results of the food cost experience of three different companies referred to as A, B and C. The food expenses analyzed were incurred by thirty ships under three different flags having correspondingly different nationalities of crew. One flag was American.

Table 5 indicates that, while the difference in cost as to ships within a fleet can apparently vary by 60 per cent, the over-all food costs vary by only 2 to 6 per cent between different owners. It would also appear that the average cost of food alone for ships' crews during 1959 was about $1.37 per man-day.

TABLE 5.

	COMPANY		
	A	B	C
Food Cost Per Man-Day			
Highest cost ship	$1.44	$1.76	$1.66
Average cost ship	1.33	1.36	1.42
Lowest cost ship	1.16	1.09	1.29
Maximum spread	.28	.65	.37
Annual cost ten ships	$233,000	$238,000	$248,000
Excess over Company A		5,000	15,000

Food Costs of Different Ships

Table 6 shows a comparison of the monthly food consumption of ten ships in one fleet. The ships are designated A, B, C, etc., and are listed in the order of their (1) economy in total cost, (2) economy in meat consumption by weight, (3) economy in consumption of other foods by weight and (4) economy in over-all consumption by weight. Costs are the actual expenses at the ports where the food was purchased. It would appear that:

1. Ship A had the lowest cost, yet was third as to over-all consumption by weight.

2. Ship B had the lowest consumption by weight, yet was second as to cost by an appreciable margin.

3. Ship G had the highest consumption by weight of all foods, yet was only seventh as to cost.

4. Although consumption by weight shows a maximum variation of 63 per cent, the maximum cost variation is only 24 per cent.

TABLE 6. COMPARATIVE FOOD COSTS AND MONTHLY CONSUMPTION
Ten Ships—1959

	COST PER MAN-DAY	MEAT KILOS	ALL OTHER EXCEPT EGGS KILOS	TOTAL KILOS
	A $1.16	F 549	B 1602	B 2442
	B 1.24	C 705	A 1932	F 2691
	C 1.25	H 743	C 2043	A 2696
	D 1.34	A 764	H 2079	C 2748
	E 1.34	B 840	D 2120	H 2822
	F 1.37	I 945	F 2142	E 3140
	G 1.39	J 950	E 2180	D 3176
	H 1.40	E 960	J 2272	J 3222
	I 1.40	D 1056	I 2532	I 3477
	J 1.44	G 1061	G 2933	G 3994
Average	$1.33	857	2184	3041
Median	1.35	892	2131	2981
Variation	.28	512	1331	1552
% Variation	24%	93%	83%	63%

Food Costs at Different Ports

From detailed consumption reports of the ten ships studied in Table 6, an average monthly consumption of the various principal foods was obtained:

Meat	Lbs.	Other	Lbs.
Beef	780	Potatoes	2,240
Mutton	280	Vegetables	1,200
Veal	160	Wheat flour	600
Pork	200	Coffee	190
Ham	100	Coffee	190
Bacon	180	Eggs (doz.)	(260)
Chops	100	Margarine	250
Poultry	160	Butter	30
Fish	310		
	2,270		4,510

Consumption figures of the ten ships showed that the average ship consumes about three tons of food monthly, consisting of one ton of meat and fish, one ton of potatoes, and one ton of other staples.

Table 7 indicates that at three random ports, all normal to the trade of these vessels, total food costs can vary by 25 per cent. However, 18 per cent is attributable to meat prices alone.

TABLE 7. FOOD COSTS AT DIFFERENT PORTS
One Month's Supply

| | GLASGOW | BALTIMORE | EMDEN | COMPOSITE | |
				HIGHS	LOWS
Meat—2,270 Lbs.	$ 860	$ 790	$ 660	$ 920	$ 630
Other—4,510	550	460	470	550	420
Totals	1,410	1,250	1,130	1,470	1,050
Amount over lowest port	280	120	0	340	−80
% over lowest port	25%	11%			

NOTE: Highs and Lows are composite totals of the highest and lowest prices of all 16 food items, regardless of the port.

Conclusions and Recommendations

As shown in this chapter, food costs are easy to measure and analyze. Consequently they are often analyzed and studied to death . . . all to the detriment of the more intangible key aspects of the business that are difficult to measure.

Total food costs of different owners apparently vary only slightly for the same number of ships. The lows and highs caused by market prices in different ports and by varying degrees of onboard efficiency seem to equalize fleet costs to a range of between $1.33 and $1.42 per man per day.

Although specific food prices can vary considerably between ports, the over-all amount in dollars is relatively small. In the three ports in which food prices were analyzed, about 75 per cent of the total cost variation was attributable to meat prices.

The lowest consumption of food by weight does not necessarily result in the lowest actual cost. The converse is also true. Food costs of individual ships, calculated from monthly consumption inventories and priced invoices, are meaningless from a cost control standpoint.

Monthly food consumption should be priced from a standard price list to give significant comparative performance.

Ships' food is generally purchased purely on price. Specifications, if any, are loose and difficult to police by remote control. Inspection of food is usually done by the crew and on ships with a quick turn round, such as tankers and ore carriers, rejection often means doing without. Food specifications are used by the Navy, hospitals and similar large institutions, and there is a good reason to believe that they could be applied to purchase contracts for vessels in liner trades.

Many foods demonstrate a consistent inconstancy in mineral and vitamin content. It would therefore appear desirable to furnish all crew members with a daily vitamin-mineral supplement, which should be introduced in a manner to preclude the implication that it is being offered to compensate for an intentional reduction in food variety.

There is no question that poor or untrained cooks spoil food, increase waste and wreck morale aboard ship. Every effort should be made to engage only the best cooks obtainable.

Shipowners should pay more attention to the possibility of obtaining improved crew performance through a program of appetizing meals planned by a competent nutritionist. Such programs of uniformly planned menus should be prepared by an independent consultant on group nutrition, with due regard for the needs of seamen and for the economics of seasonal changes in the market prices of various foods.

CHAPTER FOUR

Maintenance

Is MAINTENANCE necessary, and if so, why and to what extent? Webster defines maintenance as the act of "holding or keeping in any given condition, especially in a state of efficiency."

What is Maintenance?

If the ship could be built as a simple, perfect tool that would never fail, break, corrode, wear or deteriorate in efficiency . . . then maintenance would obviously be unnecessary. However, the designing of a thing which is at once perfect and simple is an extremely difficult task. Most anyone can design a complicated device. In Rube Goldberg's famous cartoons all of his complicated mechanisms performed the intended final function . . . but none of them were simple or sound.

At every stage of design the engineer has to make important decisions, always on the basis of imperfect knowledge. He must perpetually balance a tendency to caution—leading perhaps to uncompetitive costs—against the risk of cutting things too fine and running into failure, disgrace and expense.

While not generally recognized or defined, every ship has a built-in maintenance load which it must carry for its entire operating life. Every stroke of the designer's pencil shapes the size of this maintenance load. When the pencil is finally laid aside, the size of the load is fixed . . . for life.

We can define maintenance as actions or efforts made beforehand to prevent, so far as humanly possible, the risk of a breakdown during a service period. We can also define the opposite of planned continuous maintenance as the manner in which many people care for their automobiles. In other words, when it breaks, have someone fix it. Sure, some time is lost, but with luck maybe it will hold together while we own it.

A system of continuous maintenance can also be defined as what we have always done to main engines. Very seldom does a main propelling steam engine break down due to causes within itself. People automatically sense the importance of the main engine. If it stops, the ship stops. So the engineers unconsciously coddle the big, shiny, simple main engine. Regularly, they check the rotor position, inspect the couplings, inspect the gears, check the sprays, test the thermometers, look at the bearings and purify the oil to antiseptic degrees. This is continuous maintenance. This is why the main engine seldom stops from a cause within itself.

But it does sometimes stop from external causes. The safety device that fails to work, the fuel oil pump with a worn-out rotor, the boiler tube which bursts from scale; all victims of no continuous maintenance, they cause the ultimate stopping of the main engine when they fail.

Several months ago, while taking a trip by air, we noticed a small card posted over the aircraft's cabin door. It was issued by the Civil Aeronautics Administration, and it said, with refreshing clarity and brevity, "This aircraft is considered Airworthy as long as it remains under the system of Continuous Maintenance." It would seem notable that the word "continuous" is used, and the word "repair" is not used.

Can Maintenance be Eliminated?

There is a temptation, when taking delivery of a new ship, to feel that the designers and builders have given us a guarantee that this beautiful new ship will be maintenance proof, foolproof, and . . . damn-fool proof. Not so! They have given an implied guarantee that they have used their best efforts to do so, and this is all that can reasonably be expected.

To paraphrase Plautus, "The Maintenance of a ship is one of the two most expensive things in the world." And we all recall J. P. Morgan's classic reply about maintenance: "Young man, if you have to count what it costs, you cannot afford a yacht."

The painful business of counting the cost of maintenance is the shipowner's task alone. Others may try to help him in bits and pieces, but usually neither he nor they will ever be able to assess the end effect of their isolated efforts on the balance sheet. Consequently, the complex problem of total maintenance must be examined by the person who does all the maintenance and pays for it. The shipowner is the only one who can possibly know what his maintenance costs are and will be, and therefore he is the only one who can balance today's capital investment against tomorrow's maintenance cost on a present worth basis.

Possibly, if ships could be designed and built in an extremely simple form, maintenance could progressively be reduced and ultimately confined to negligible proportions. If the finished ship could be as simple as a cube of stainless steel used for a paperweight, then, of course, maintenance could be completely eliminated. The stainless steel paperweight would far outlast the twenty- or thirty-year life we expect of a ship; in fact, without much risk, we could predict that the paperweight might last ten or twenty centuries without maintenance, polishing, of course, excepted.

However, the rapidly changing shape of world trade, social advances and accelerating technical progress have made the ship a more complicated brute with each new design. Generally, each new vessel produced is more competitive economically than the last design, even though it might have a higher built-in maintenance load due to its increased complexity.

In past years, a ship might have been produced through the design efforts of a few dozen hull and engine draftsmen, the main engine and practically all component parts being constructed right in the shipbuilder's works from his own designs. As an extreme present-day comparison, let us look at the slightly greater number of people who were involved in the design and construction of the nuclear icebreaker *Lenin*. There were 30 research establishments, 60 design bureaus, 51 economic councils and 250 plants and factories.

No shortage of talent here; only 391 different agencies, each probably having some hundreds to thousands of technicians, all contributing to the complexity and the final built-in maintenance work load of this one ship. As Plautus once specifically observed, "Who wishes to give himself an abundance of trouble, let him equip these two things, a ship and a woman. No two things involve more bother, for neither is ever sufficiently adorned."

The Utility Factor

When we are faced with the cost of maintenance of a ship and particularly with the unpleasantness of having to take a ship out of service for a few days for some needed maintenance, it is easy to get into a frame of mind where we become critical of the designers, the builders, the ship's officers or the person in charge of the ship's maintenance. We get the uneasy feeling that the system has broken down, or that someone is not doing his job properly, or this trouble would not have happened to us.

Let us look for a moment at the utility factor to which we subject the ship. Take a bulk carrier operating from South America to United

States ports, which makes about 24 round voyages annually. Such
a ship will be operating about as follows: 250 days at sea; 50 days
steaming in rivers; 55 days loading and discharging; 10 days out of
service for maintenance, accidents, etc.

This means that the ship's propulsion machinery is being utilized
for 83 per cent of its total life, about 70 per cent at peak load. The
ship's hull, boilers and much of the auxiliary machinery are being
utilized for 97 per cent of the time.

Our modern automobile, which seems generally conceded to be a
model of engineering perfection, even though it breaks down once
in a while at quite unexpected moments, and whose mechanical and
thermal efficiencies seem to deteriorate in direct proportion to the age
of the vehicle, seems to have a rather different utility factor. Our own
automobile, which is not unlike all the rest, has run 70,000 miles in six
years, which is about 25 hours per month. This is a utility factor of
only 3½ per cent or about 1/24 of what we expect from a bulk
carrier or tanker.

Why Seaworthiness?

If an ocean-going ship could survive its twenty or thirty years' life
span with a complete disregard for maintenance, then probably no
shipowner would employ any maintenance (except for aesthetic
reasons) even though the ship would have only residual or scrap value
at the end of its life. This presumes, of course, that the safety, efficiency
and seaworthiness of the ship would not deteriorate along with the
depreciation in the vessel's condition. This is, perhaps, the heart of the
matter, and, with certain exceptions, we know that the ship's safety,
efficiency and seaworthiness depend on the material condition of the
vessel's hull and its machinery.

Why the ship should be efficient in speed, fuel consumption and
working cargo needs no explanation here. But the question will be
asked, "Why must the ship be safe and seaworthy?" Until about 1850,
ships were probably only as safe and seaworthy as the owner or
master deemed necessary to protect his investment.

In Great Britain, the Mercantile Marine Act of 1850 and the
Merchant Shipping Act of 1854 constituted the first serious attempts
to provide for the safety of life and goods at sea. For the first time,
masters and mates of foreign-going ships were required to qualify by
examination. The Merchant Shipping Amendment Act of 1862 in-
stituted examinations for engineers, and the first chief engineer's license
was granted to one Thomas Thaw on April 15, 1863.

In the United States, the public, especially the traveling public, was similarly taking an increasingly dimmer view of the prospects of death by fire, boiler explosion and drowning. It was strongly suspected in some circles that boiler explosions might not be fortuitous acts of God, but rather that they were caused by poor design, defective materials or low water. The first law in the United States to provide for the better security of passengers on steam vessels was contained in the Act of Congress passed July 7, 1838.

As could be expected, the first attempt to legislate control of such explosive and controversial matters, honeycombed with politics and steeped in vested interest, left much to be desired. John H. Morrison's *History of American Steam Navigation* (Bibliog. 7) describes the mechanics of steamboat inspection in those days in few words.

"The inspectors were appointed by the district judges of the United States Courts in the several districts, and were paid the sum of five dollars by the owner of the vessel for each inspection. To show the utter worthlessness of the inspections at this date, and the formal manner in which they were carried out, the testimony, in part, of an inspector, given at a coroner's inquest, where several lives were lost by the burning of a large passenger steamboat on the Atlantic coast, will suffice.

'We never condemned any boat. We have restricted them to a certain amount of steam.'
'When you inspect a boat you look at the wood and do nothing else?'
'Yes, we take our fees.'
'How do you examine the hull of a vessel?'
'Why, I examine it with my eyes. I go and inquire the boat's age; I examine the hull and I look at the engine. How much do you suppose I am to do for five dollars?' "

Subsequent interesting steps in the early American attempt to legislate safety and seaworthiness were as follows:

March 3, 1843. Created a board of examiners to determine whether hydrostatic pressure, or what alternative plan, was best for testing the strength of marine boilers. (Louisiana had required hydrostatic testing since 1834, flowing from the laws of France which required a test of three times the working pressure.)

August 30, 1852. Required that all engineers and pilots of passenger steam vessels be licensed by the local inspectors.
Required the hydrostatic testing of marine boilers and the stamping of boiler plate with the quality of iron and manufacturer's name.

October 30, 1852. Required bell signals to be used when passing in narrow channels and for the bell to be sounded every two minutes when running in fog.

Required that a bright white light be carried on the stem and another on the mast near the stern.

October 9, 1854. Provided for the steam whistle to be used in place of the bell.

June 4, 1864. Ferryboats and tugboats brought under the jurisdiction of the Supervising Inspectors.

July 25, 1866. Freight steamers brought under the jurisdiction of the Supervising Inspectors.

Act of 1871. Required masters and chief mates of steam vessels to be licensed by the local inspectors.

Required all seagoing steamers to have not less than three watertight bulkheads made of plate iron.

Required that steam boilers be fitted with pressure gauges, lock-up safety valves and low-water gauges (all subjects of a patent right).

The fact (in America) that marine engineers were licensed officers some nineteen years before the masters and mates probably made its small contribution to effectively inhibiting any spirit of togetherness that might otherwise have existed between the deck and the engineering departments. The law of August 30, 1852, recognized the engineers and pilots as the only licensed officers and identified the master as being the representative of the owner on board. As such, the master was responsible, with the owner, for all damages flowing from his election to pursue any voyage in contravention to the advice of the engineer or pilot that further navigation might be unsafe.

Subsequent legislation by individual maritime countries, usually flowing from international agreements on minimum standards for safety at sea, has resulted in substantial national policing of ships' safety and seaworthiness. It has usually taken some shattering sea tragedies to trigger these international conferences on safety.

International Safety of Life at Sea Convention

The International Safety of Life at Sea Convention (SOLASC) of 1948, of which all the major maritime nations are signatories, contains some rather broad regulations. For example, the contracting governments undertake to promulgate all laws necessary to give the conference full effect so as to insure that, from the point of view of safety of life, their ships are fit for the intended service. The conference delegates the inspection of ships to the country of registry and prescribes the following certificates which must be maintained in a valid condition as to each vessel:

1. **A Safety Certificate.** Which sets forth that the ship has been surveyed and complies with the provisions of the Convention.

2. **A Safety Equipment Certificate.** Which sets forth that the lifesaving appliances, fire-extinguishing appliances and certain navigation equipment are in compliance with the provisions of the Convention.

3. **A Safety Radio Telegraphy Certificate.** Which sets forth that the radio equipment is in compliance with the provisions of the Convention.

4. **An Exemption Certificate.** Which sets forth the extent of any requirement of the Convention from which the vessel may be exempted.

The broad minimum requirements of the International Convention are, of course, the framework of each individual country's safety requirements. Each country then amplifies these basic requirements to suit its own individual philosophies, some to encyclopedic proportions.

Carriage of Goods by Sea Act (COGSA)

Exoneration from liability for the cargo losses of others is usually sought by the shipowner under the provisions of what is known as the Carriage of Goods by Sea Act, April 16, 1936 (COGSA). This Act arose from enactments of the Brussels Convention in 1924, which was subsequently adopted by the principal maritime nations of the world. The provisions of COGSA require, among other things, that the carrier exercise due diligence before and at the beginning of the voyage to make the ship seaworthy. This obligation of the shipowner cannot be delegated to another. It is further provided that neither the carrier nor the ship shall be liable for loss or damage of cargo resulting from unseaworthiness unless caused by want of due diligence on the part of the carrier to make the ship seaworthy. When the loss or damage has resulted from unseaworthiness, however, the carrier has the burden of proving the exercise of due diligence. If this burden is sustained, it is provided that neither the carrier nor the ship shall be responsible for loss or damage resulting from a series of specified events, including, among others, "perils, dangers, and accidents of the sea or other navigable waters," "act of God" or "latent defects not discoverable by due diligence." There are, of course, many other provisions of COGSA, but, for the purposes of this discussion, only the foregoing have been specifically identified.

A Compelling Reason for Good Maintenance

Shipowner's Limitation of Liability Statutes have been on the United States federal statute books since 1851. The purpose of these statutes, as pointed out by James L. Adams (Bibliog. 8), has been recognized on many occasions by the United States Supreme Court as being "to encourage investments in ships and their employment in commerce."

Provisions of these statutes permit the liability of a shipowner for losses of life and property by others, if incurred "without the privity or knowledge" of the shipowner, to be limited to the value of the interest of the shipowner in the vessel and her freight then pending. The terms "privity" and "knowledge" of the shipowner have been defined and applied by the courts in innumerable cases. Disregarding many refinements that often are involved, these terms mean in the case of a corporate shipowner simply that the negligence of a high-ranking managerial employee (whose scope of authority includes supervision over the phase of the business out of which loss occurred) binds the corporate shipowner. If the negligence of such an employee proximately caused or contributed to the loss, the shipowner is not entitled to limit his liability under these statutes.

If a court finds the shipowner is liable or, in other words, should not be exonerated from liability, and if the shipowner has petitioned to limit his liability, the court then proceeds to determine whether or not the shipowner has the right to limit such liability. If this right is found to exist, the shipowner's liability is limited generally to the value of the ship after the casualty plus the freight then pending. If personal injury or death claims are involved, liability of the shipowner for such claims cannot be limited in the case of any seagoing vessel to a total amount less than $60 per ton of the vessel's gross tonnage.

It would seem, then, that the shipowner is rather definitely bound to make his ship safe and seaworthy and to properly man, equip and supply the ship not only by law but also by fear of incurring almost unlimited liability. Furthermore, in litigation that may arise out of any accident or casualty, the burden of proof often falls on the shipowner to show affirmatively that he has used due diligence to make his ship seaworthy and to properly man, equip and supply it.

In the foregoing, we have seen some rather cogent reasons why the shipowner must maintain his vessels in a safe, efficient and seaworthy manner, and to maintain them in such a state requires maintenance, until something better is invented.

Time for Soul Searching

Fundamentally, the subject of planned maintenance is nothing new. The requirements of periodic survey by the classification societies and various national regulatory agencies are all aimed, be it unwittingly, at planned maintenance. However, the operation of ships is seldom so regular, so smooth, so predictable or so local that controlled planned maintenance can in fact be carried out. Ships have little resemblance to aircraft, trains or trucks in the matter of trying to fit maintenance into the operational requirements of the equipment. Here lies a real challenge that can be met and overcome. All that is required is some careful analysis pointed at separating our objectives, targets and individual problems.

The complex nature of the ship maintenance problem is well illustrated by the reception which an excellent paper (Bibliog. 9) on the subject received at the 1959 SNAME convention in New York. The purpose of this paper was to open up the over-all subject of ship maintenance for discussion, leading to a better understanding and increased knowledge of the subject by all concerned. Admirably the paper closed with the hope that it would draw criticism which would in turn bring forward new ideas.

The discussion of this paper attracted eleven brave discussers who presented ten very interesting and constructive pages of suggestions and criticism. Of these eleven discussers, only one man was in that eternally lonesome position of being finally and totally responsible for, to, and with a shipowner for the safety, reliability and seaworthiness of ships. In his discussion, Mr. Nicholas Bachko quickly got down to fundamentals, and with refreshing objectivity he said:

"I have before me a quotation by A. E. Perlman, President, New York Central, as follows: 'After you have done a thing the same way for two years, look it over carefully. After five years, look at it with suspicion. And after ten years, throw it away and start all over again.'

"In the maintenance and repair field we have been doing things the same way for much longer than ten years, and this paper, though perhaps not a perfect vehicle, makes a plea for self-examination with a view to change."

Why Silence?

With such a tempting piece of bait as the subject of maintenance thrown on the table, why should scores of engineers, whose lifework and specialty is maintenance, remain silent? There are perhaps several reasons for this.

Firstly, because of the highly competitive nature of their business, shipowners and their maintenance staffs are understandably reluctant to discuss their maintenance problems with others and particularly to air their troubles in public. A discussion of such matters will usually be peculiar to the trade of the vessel, and the costs and problems of the trade will be of intense interest to the competition in many indirect, as well as obvious, ways. Consequently, the shipowners' staff operates in an attitude of *en garde* as though taking too literally the words of Matthew 12:30, "He that is not with me is against me." If all of the shipowner's maintenance troubles were a matter of public knowledge, there is the possibility that he would immediately be harrassed by the claims of shippers, charterers, insurers, surveyors, inspectors, passengers and any other agency or person whose interests were not parallel to his. The end effect of the end of this privity would be the end of business. From a maintenance standpoint, however, it is not unlike being sick, but being unable to tell the doctor your symptoms.

Secondly, the engineer responsible for the maintenance of a fleet of ships is in quite a different position from the design engineer, the sales engineer or the operating engineer. After an error in judgment he cannot say, "So sorry, we'll give you a new part provided you pay for the labor of installation." He cannot say, "Oh, how stupid of me! Charge it to crew negligence." He is at the end of the line with his back against the wall all the time. Under the Carriage of Goods by Sea Act, the Superintendent Engineer is that certain high-ranking managerial employee whose negligence (or error in judgment which might later be equated as negligence) can prevent the shipowner from limiting his liability. The loneliness of this position of responsibility is not conducive to getting one's name in the paper.

Thirdly, we must consider the widely varying maintenance requirements of different ships in different trades under different conditions and circumstances. For example, a ship operating in known foul harbors might have to open all heat exchangers quarterly for cleaning, while a ship running in clean, deep water might get by for a year without adverse effect. Paints and bottom coatings good enough for deep water operating might be totally inadequate for navigation in sandy shoal rivers. The measurement of machinery wear that might be easily accomplished in a vessel with much port time could be economically disastrous to a ship with extremely limited port time.

All these constantly changing variables act individually and collectively to frustrate the person responsible for maintenance and to give him a feeling of the hopelessness of ever achieving a *steady state* of controlled planned maintenance. These factors also act to deter the engineer from discussing his maintenance problems with others, for, compared with ships in more fortunate circumstances, it might appear that he is wasting money.

A Clue to the Problem

Notwithstanding this real or imaginary gag which has been placed on the mouths of many engineers in the operating and maintenance field, there are a great number of excellent writings available. They cannot be found in one library or in one country, but a diligent search will turn them up.

The available literature on this subject is excellent because it has been written by persons with the courage and sagacity to write on important subjects, which always contain some element of controversy. A sample of some of the worthwhile writings that have recently been published are:

The Preservation of Oil Tanker Hulls, by John Lamb & E. V. Mathias. Transactions N. E. Coast Institution of Engineers & Shipbuilders, Vol. 69, 1953.

Some Aspects of Ship Bottom Corrosion, by Paul Ffield. Transactions SNAME, Volume 58, 1950.

Some Aspects of Propeller Deterioration and Its Prevention, by P. Ffield, L. M. Mosher, and A. J. O'Neil. SNAME New England Section, May, 1956.

Some Considerations of Wear in Marine Gearing, by W. H. Darlington. Transactions I. Mar. E., September, 1956.

Some Teething Troubles in Post-War Reduction Gears, by S. Archer. Transactions I. Mar. E., September, 1956.

Fouling of Marine Type Heat Exchangers, by H. E. Bethon. Transactions ASME, October, 1949.

Some Unusual Ship and Machinery Defects, Their Investigation and Cure, A Symposium. Transactions I. Mar. E., February, 1953.

All of the above articles are supercharged with interest to the owner or operator of a ship. Indeed, they should also be required reading for the student, the designer, the engine builder and the shipbuilder. The titles of these papers cry out that maintenance and material problems remain unsolved and require collective thought and solution. They also give us some clues in defining the control areas of our maintenance problem. These areas seem to be *corrosion, wear* and *abuse.*

Corrosion

Probably the principal diseases to which ships are subject are corrosion, wear, fatigue and abuse. Ships today are constructed principally of steel, and it should be remembered that iron and steel are man-made refinements of natural substances, and their existence as such is *contrary* to the processes of nature. Steel is created from stable natural ferric oxides, and there is a compelling tendency for it to revert to the oxide form. Ferric oxide is familiar to everyone as common rust. Sea water, the natural marine environment, contains about 3 per cent salt and has a high electrical conductivity, thus making it one of the most corrosive natural agencies. It is a small wonder that ships have a number of corrosion problems that must be solved if they are to operate safely and economically.

As suggested by Adams and Hudson (Bibliog. 10), one of the first questions that comes to mind is whether the corrosion of steel in ships could be decreased or eliminated by altering the composition of the steel. Very broadly, the answer to this would seem to be "no." Exhaustive testing and research on this question in several countries agree in showing that, when bare steels are submerged in sea water, there is no great difference in their resistence to corrosion unless a fairly high percentage of chromium is added to the steel. The addition of 3 per cent chromium only halves the corrosion rate. Even the use of 18 per cent chromium and 8 per cent nickel fails to solve the problem, for, while the general corrosion rate is less, it is achieved only at the expense of greater vulnerability to pitting. Even without doing any figures, we know that the use of rust-resistant steels for general shipbuilding would not now be economically justified, and, further, we also know that the available supply of these materials would not permit their use. Consequently, for practical purposes, it would seem better to pay strict attention to the efficiencies of the protective measures adopted.

It is difficult to suggest a mean rate of corrosion for ship steel since this depends on many factors, such as abrasion and different environmental conditions, all of which vary the rate. An analysis of plate renewals made by the ship research section of *Lloyd's Register* has shown, for example, that colliers require about three times as many shell-plating renewals as do deep sea ships. The difference is accounted for by the much more frequent rubbing of the colliers against their berths and other ships and their frequent groundings at loading berths, which remove the paint besides scouring the steel.

The foregoing should focus our attention on the point that the removal of paint is one of the commonest reasons for corrosion, particularly where other conditions occur to accelerate it. There is very good reason to believe that most hull painting, and bottom painting in particular, is accomplished under circumstances less than ideal.

Take 75,000 square feet of steel surface, place two-thirds of it in semidarkness and very near the ground, then cover the surface with slime, mud and oil and throw on a film of water from condensation over the loose paint and rust. Then, in 24 to 36 hours, try to prepare this surface and paint it with at least two coats of paint so that it will withstand submersion in salt water for one year without fouling or corrosion. These are the circumstances under which a ship's bottom is often repainted. It would appear that corrosion is a major problem worthy of concentrated effort and continuous study by any marine maintenance staff.

Wear

Seagoing marine engineers have long prided themselves on being able to "keep the job going." This task has been accomplished most successfully and has created a tradition of unparalleled improvisation that was, and is, an invaluable part of the young engineer's training.

However, as William Falconer (Bibliog. 11) so clearly points out, much of the unique improvisation and heavy maintenance that was in the past accomplished by the ship's stalwart engineers, was possible only because of the large tolerances in the strength of working parts. For example, this allowed piston rods to be machined and refitted to their parent equipage many times. The use of a spare was, in many instances, regarded with regret as a reflection on the craftsman's ability to repair the original part. This explains why the "fitters bench" used to be the recruiting grounds for young junior engineers.

Modern marine engineering, because of design improvements and better economy that is mandatory for competitive reasons, has greatly reduced these tolerances and has in any case changed from a predominantly reciprocating plant to a predominantly rotary one with much higher speeds. Other fields of engineering and transportation, where high performance and light weight have greater advantages, have produced a "limited life and replacement" philosophy which has seeped steadily into the marine field, and will probably continue to do so at an increasing rate.

What Standard?

It would seem that the first thing which must be decided in planning a maintenance program is the standard of maintenance that is desired. For example, the antiseptic standard of painting and polishing required for the promenade of a passenger ship is neither necessary nor economically allowable on the deck of a tramp. Such variations in degree are harder to define in the case of machinery, but it can be done. To be effective, planned maintenance must save work and/or money. An extreme view might be that the only criterion by which the adequacy of a maintenance program can be judged is the down-time or off-hire per year. This, however, is affected by many extraneous factors such as the adequacy of the personnel (including the deck officers) and the efficiency and work load in the shipyard dry-docking the vessel (not to mention the weather).

Perhaps an acceptable standard of maintenance could be defined as that which requires only a minimum reasonable amount of down-time without entering the area of diminishing returns.

The Time Factor

In the how, where and when to accomplish necessary maintenance, the *when,* or time factor, seems an uncommonly important one in the area of grouping our maintenance for analysis. In the case of ships we have three rather clearly defined periods during which different types of maintenance are usually carried out. They are: 1. in dry dock, 2. alongside or at moorings (at extended notice for main engines) and 3. at sea.

Certainly the maintenance work to hull, shafts, propeller, rudder and underwater fittings which must be done on dry dock assumes critical importance with regard to the time used. All time used for this maintenance is down-time, and, theoretically, if there are no breakdowns in service, then the time used in dry dock will be the only down-time.

The maintenance work carried out in port, with main engines secured, also assumes great importance. It is this category of maintenance which assures the reliability of the propelling machinery at sea.

In the third maintenance period at sea, maintenance is rather restricted to work of a routine and minor nature. For one thing, during this period 50 per cent of the crew, including most of the officers, concern themselves with the navigation and operation of the ship, rather than with the maintenance function.

Instructions and Records

Clear and simple maintenance instruction is almost nonexistent on ships today. Most chief engineers are given a wide latitude to inaugurate and execute their own maintenance systems. Detailed maintenance instructions are usually contained in the instruction books furnished by the manufacturer of each piece of equipment. In a noble effort to cover every last detail, however, most manufacturers do not give sufficient treatment to fundamentals or "pitfalls." Instruction books of encyclopedic proportions are, therefore, seldom read until after the fact of a breakdown.

Probably the reason why simple instructions on maintenance fundamentals and pitfalls have not been written is because it is difficult to write something that is simple and clear. We are reminded of Voltaire when he wrote, "You will have to pardon the length of my letter as I don't have time to write a short one."

In days gone by, on ships whose maintenance was performed principally by the crew, some owners used what was called a "Condition Report Book" to get a current picture of the condition of all machinery and equipment and to plan future maintenance. This was a large book having a page for each item of machinery and also listing all the spare parts, of which there were not many. In ideal practice this book was filled out accurately and faithfully by the chief engineer in a beautiful Spencerian hand and mailed forthwith to the home office every six months. Until 1935, this system was probably sufficient.

Probably the minimum record-keeping of any value that is done by some owners consists of copies of all maintenance bills and all narrative survey reports. Other owners add to these ships' certificates and logbooks, performance reports, boiler water condition reports, machinery condition reports, and so forth.

These records are more or less historical in nature and are either so general or so limited that the entire maintenance picture cannot be seen even with an extensive file search. Nowhere in this vast sea of paper is there anything so delightfully simple and clear as the sticker which a service station puts on the door of each car to show when it was last lubricated and when it is next due.

The sacrosanct ship's logbook, which originated on the sailing ship as a journal of the master's guesses as to where he might be, now serves approximately the same purpose in the engine room. When an instantaneous value on an uncalibrated thermometer is read by a disinterested person of untested vision from a distance of ten feet with a dim flashlight, the resulting entry in the log is worthy of exactly the attention it gets from those who never read it. Nowhere in this sea of instruments is there anything so delightfully simple and accurate as the integrating kilowatt-hour meter used in every house.

Administrative staffs are usually kept to a minimum for many reasons, including Parkinson's Law. The majority of people employed in the engineering departments of steamship companies are engaged in the task of processing various bills for payment and in supporting these bills with enough documentary evidence to demonstrate that the service was properly ordered, the service was actually performed and that the price was fair and reasonable. There are accounting functions of "supporting expense" and "preventing fraud." It is doubtful whether they contribute to the improvement of engineering practices or the intelligent and economical planning of a future maintenance program.

Apparent Maintenance Costs

Table 8 shows the results of a detailed analysis made of 532 individual items of maintenance cost incurred by two 35,000-ton ships over a period of about two years. The cost categories selected were admittedly arbitrary but were based on preliminarily selected cost control parameters. They are:

Underwater Corrosion. Protection of bottom and outside hull, ground tackle, rudder, zincs, sea valves, bilge keels.

Underwater Wear. Maintenance of propeller, shaft, stern bearing, rudder bearings, other moving fittings.

Tanks and Tank Piping. Preservation of cargo tanks, ballast tanks, water tanks, associated piping.

Heat Exchangers. Preservation of water boxes, water sides and salt water piping thereto.

Surveys and Safety. Surveyors' fees of every nature, maintenance of lifesaving and fire-fighting gear, radio station, radar, r.d.f., navigating instruments.

Machinery. Maintenance and parts replacement to main engine, turbines, pumps and all other rotating machinery.

Steam Boilers. Cleaning and maintenance of fire and watersides, refractory, casings, mountings and fuel-burning equipment.

Electrical. Cleaning of motors and generators, reinsulation, renewal of bearings and limited life items, testing, including all fans and blowers.

Working Tackle. Mooring winches and mooring wires, hatch tackle, gangways, etc.

Hotel Equipment. Maintenance of ranges and ovens, food machines, ice machines, air conditioning, chairs and furniture.

Hull Miscellaneous. Maintenance of miscellaneous minor items, ladders, steps, fittings.

Overtime To Save Time. Overtime charges which were less than the charter hire thereby saved.

TABLE 8.   APPARENT MAINTENANCE COSTS
Two-Year Period 1957/59

	SHIP A	SHIP B
Underwater Corrosion	$ 49,614	$ 48,144
Underwater Wearing Parts	11,441	1,286
Tanks and Tank Piping	0	2,524
Heat Exchangers and S W Piping	4,087	9,952
Surveys and Safety	2,701	4,546
Machinery	37,072	38,091
Steam Boilers	21,158	9,601
Electrical	4,889	5,388
Working Tackle	1,962	66
Hotel Equipment	602	1,062
Hull Miscellaneous	2,547	6,282
Overtime to Save Time	7,934	9,639
Total	$144,007	$136,581

The small difference between vessels in some categories is not too significant and, in most cases, is attributable to a portion of the inspection or maintenance expense being related to an insurance claim.

Hidden Maintenance Costs

The 532 individual items of maintenance cost analyzed in this study constitute a formidable list. On a ten-ship fleet basis there would possibly be 2,500 items of expense. This number of individual contracts, which they are for the most part, results in tens of thousands of pieces of paper being handled by hundreds of people over the course of a year. Ships' officers, superintendents, agents, clerks and accountants by the score all must handle their own particular size and color of paper necessary to request, approve, order, receipt, bill, initial, pay and mail a check to someone for furnishing a service. To the delight of the paper manufacturers, all this quiet efficiency goes on whether the item is a $5,000 motor or a 5¢ spring.

With such a vast amount of activity connected with spending an apparent $75,000 a year per ship on maintenance, it would seem reasonable to expect that a shipowner should know where the money is going. This is questionable, however, for all this myriad activity is primarily concerned with accounting support, not maintenance planning.

On the other hand, a bill for $100,000 comes in once a year for insurance premiums on a ship. The bill is paid, the policy filed, and only two or three people even know it happened. For a whole year not another penny of administrative cost will result.

Using Ship A as an example (Table 8), we see that $49,600 was spent on attempting to prevent underwater corrosion. Of this amount $16,200 was used in the purchase of paint. Now, in a completely separate account of another department, we can see that an additional $25,500 was spent on paint that was applied by the ship's crew over the same period for the same purpose—to fight corrosion.

We know (see Chapter II) that the ten men engaged in deck maintenance cost $1,747 a month, or about $42,000 during this two-year period, to apply $25,500 worth of paint.

Therefore, even though weeks were spent in analyzing all the money spent by the engineering department, the figure of $49,600 does not even approximate the true total spent on underwater and hull corrosion. A more accurate figure would be:

Shipyard cost	$33,400
Paint furnished	16,200
Crew labor	42,000
Paint used	25,500
Total	$117,100

Conclusions and Recommendations

Every ship has a built-in maintenance work load, the size of which is determined by: the excellence of design, the quality of materials used and the quality of workmanship, the excellence of the maintenance program, the quality of the maintenance personnel and the time available for maintenance in the ship's schedule.

Until substantially maintenance-free ships are developed, maintenance will be necessary to (1) protect the capital investment and (2) keep the ship seaworthy. International and national laws require ships to be maintained in a seaworthy condition. The shipowner must be able to demonstrate that his ship was seaworthy in order to limit his liability for losses caused by or suffered on his ship.

Varying standards of maintenance are appropriate depending on a vessel's type, age and trade. In all cases, however, the desirable standard is that which provides the optimum end economic results for the given vessel and circumstances. With regard to components affecting operational reliability, it will usually be found that the highest practical standard produces the best end economic results. With regard to areas which can be disassociated from operational reliability and seaworthiness, it will be found that the desirable standard can be accurately defined only after measuring expected life and making capitalized cost and present worth comparisons. In any event, the standard of maintenance desired must be defined. In the absence of such definition, the program will automatically take the shape of little more than a combination of the minimum requirements of law plus "Breakdown Maintenance."

The utility factor to which a ship is subjected is extreme compared with most industrial machinery and tools. Operating a ship for twenty years compares with operating the same road tractor for seventy years or an automobile for four hundred years.

The operation of cars and trucks is probably the best example of the practice of "breakdown maintenance." The operation of passenger aircraft is probably the best example of planned "preventive maintenance." There is good reason to believe that many of the maintenance philosophies and techniques of the aircraft industry in the area of component reliability could be adapted with economic advantage to the marine industry.

The amount of down-time allowed (a) in shipyard and (b) at moorings is extremely important in the determination of the scope and quality of the maintenance program that can be undertaken.

Problems of machinery wear appear to be changing along with changes in the type of machinery. Wear can be reduced or minimized by good operating and maintenance procedures. The practice of "repair by replacement" will continue to gain favor as labor costs rise faster than material costs.

Clear and simple operating and maintenance instructions that will protect the personnel from Fundamental Errors and Basic Perils are virtually nonexistent. The large "NO SMOKING" sign on the deck of a tanker is one of the few warnings that is not buried in an unread instruction book. A basic operating manual for the use of the ship's officers is mandatory and it should consist of a minimum number of critical subjects, properly and clearly written. The areas covered should be only those basic principles which, if forgotten or ignored, result in damage, delay and tragedy.

Realistic maintenance objectives can be erected only by calling things what they are and eliminating archaic labels. Substitute "Maintenance Department" for "Engineering Department" and "Fault" for "Repair." The value of this mental catharsis will soon be apparent in creative attitude, clarified objectives and improved performance.

The marine maintenance staff suffers some understandable frustrations. They are called engineers, yet they do not create or build anything. They are held responsible for seaworthiness clearly and maintenance vaguely, yet spend much of their time in "accounting support" duties. They are selected for superior ability and experience, yet are paid in many cases only half as much as the ship's officers they supervise. The existence of such an unclear structure acts effectively to confuse responsibilities, objectives and problem solutions.

The persons responsible for administering the maintenance function are the conservators of some 90 per cent of our controllable expense. They should be compensated in proportion to the critically high importance of this function and commensurately high performance be demanded of them.

Corrosion is the number one problem in ship maintenance, accounting for some 60 to 70 per cent of the true maintenance dollar. The many forms in which corrosion attacks, and the many accounts in which corrosion costs are buried, completely camouflage the magnitude of this expense to the shipowner. An experienced corrosion engineer or metallurgist should be employed to devote full time to the solution of ship corrosion problems. These problems are principally electrochemical in nature, not mechanical.

Standards of maintenance and operating record systems are nonexistent. Current record systems have grown like Topsy with the complexity of machinery and operations, but they are historical and financial in nature and are not geared directly to planned maintenance programs. The entire record-keeping system in use should be objectively analyzed. It is possible that recording integrating instruments aboard ship would provide much more accurate and valuable data at great savings in time. Additionally, suitable flexible cost coding can eliminate the mass of accounting support documents that fill the unread files of most maintenance departments.

Current industry accounting procedures do not reveal maintenance costs either in total or by major cost categories. Accordingly, all aspects of the function of maintenance cost accounting should be objectively re-examined. Simple coding systems exist that will compel all maintenance costs, including those presently buried in other accounts, to fall into their proper, easily identifiable slot. The slots must be keyed to the controllable cause of the particular maintenance expense, if any degree of cost control is to be achieved. Successful systems of this type are based on the simple but fundamental principle that "ink dries but cards can be shuffled." A flexible and accurate system of maintenance cost accounting will automatically produce the answers necessary to drastically reduce maintenance costs and to develop progressive, new construction standards.

CHAPTER FIVE

Materials

T<small>HE</small> search for the best material for a given job is not a new one. It has been going on since the first man dropped out of a tree.

Problem Solving

This continuous and incessant searching for better materials and tools with which to do a job has been one of the principal creative factors in the development of our civilization today. It is recorded that Archimedes developed his well-known principle while searching for a way to test the purity of gold in his King's Crown. So it has been with the majority of inventions and improvements. First a need is revealed, followed by the definition of the problem. Then targets are erected as aims for creative thought leading to multiple solutions and ultimately the best solution.

Quality

As expressed in purchasing vernacular, the word "quality" has a somewhat different meaning from its colloquial usage. Quality for us does not necessarily mean the best of its kind, but rather the best grade of material to fulfill, but not exceed, the requirements of the use for which it is intended. We cannot reach this technical and economic equilibrium if quality standards are established arbitrarily through inertia, custom, prejudice or personal relationships with vendors rather than on a basis of utility and value. Teamwork and open minds are absolutely essential when dealing with quality standards, which ideally should be worked out by organized and impartial test programs.

Materials of Maintenance

The materials used in the operation of a ship are many and varied, but they can be classified into eighteen major categories for consumption or cost control purposes. The groups would seem to be:

Chinaware	Linens	Paints and equipment
Cleaning supplies	Medical supplies	Pipe and fittings
Fire-fighting gear	Miscellaneous	Ropes and cordage
Galley equipment	Navigating equipment	Stock, metal
Hardware	Oils and greases	Tableware
Lifesaving gear	Packings	Tools

It is quite noticeable that, except for medical, linens, chinaware and tableware, all the remaining materials are used in the *maintenance* of the physical ship. They are all used to preserve, patch, repair or replace parts and areas of the ship in order to maintain a continuous state of efficiency called seaworthiness.

Improvement

Since World War II an imposing array of hitherto unknown materials have been developed. Most of these are not only better and longer lasting than their forerunners, but cheaper as well. To anyone familiar with the ravenous appetite of the corrosive marine environment, many of the new materials that are available almost cry out the savings in maintenance labor and replacement cost that will result from their use. Only a few of these are:

Inflatable rafts	Extreme-pressure oils	Plastic hardware
Plastic lifeboats	Oil stern bearings	Tank coatings
Synthetic cordage	Nickel alloy propellers	Plastic pipe
Non-fouling alloys	Better refractories	Improved steel coatings

For several good reasons, most improved materials, tools and equipment appear in other industries years before they gravitate into the marine field. We are reminded of a problem we once had to find a method of internal nondestructive visual examination of heat exchanger tubes having an inside diameter of only ½ inch. We found the answer in our doctor's office—his cystoscope. We also found that this simple instrument had been used for years by gun makers—for examining their gun barrels. The marine climate is such that we unintentionally limit our thinking to looking for better mousetraps, when our objective should be to find a better way to kill mice.

Conservatism and Progress

The propensity of the marine industry for conservatism in the selection of materials is almost legend. We know that turpentine, Stockholm tar, bronze, manila, flax and cotton performed acceptably through the nineteenth century. This, of course, gives us confidence in these materials. With the compelling responsibility to send only seaworthy ships to sea, there is also some satisfaction in knowing that we cannot be criticized for using the old "tried and true" materials.

Commander G. W. R. Nicholl (Bibliog. 12), in his most interesting book on the development and design of inflatable lifesaving equipment, *Survival at Sea,* shows us with remarkable insight some of the reasons for the obvious conservatism of our marine society:

"The sailor is traditionally cautious and conservative. These are characteristics born of long contact with an element which permits no liberties; an element quick to anger, a fury against whom the finest tempered steel is of no avail; even in its most halcyon mood, the sea's smile is reserved and distant. However solidly strong the ship, it can only be hoped that the sea will tolerate it for a lifetime, for it might well be engulfed on its maiden voyage. Progress in maritime matters is, therefore, generally evolutionary and not revolutionary. It cannot thus be wondered that innovations are accepted with caution."

It seems a pity, however, when we let such considerations force us into purchasing decisions which are wrong not only technically but economically as well. Not enough of us seem to realize that 90 per cent of all the scientists and engineers who ever lived are alive today and produce better materials in every field with each passing hour.

No Standards or Guarantees

The largest dollar volume of materials purchased is in the area of marine paints and coatings, whose basic purpose is to provide a barrier between ferrous metals and the marine environment. Let us take a look at the typical sales effort of several ma·ine paint manufacturers. Their advertising is usually confined to full-page advertisements in the marine magazines, most of the page being filled with a pretty picture of a new ship.

Manufacturer Able says: "There's always a welcome for the man from Able. His advice on painting problems is held in high esteem."

Manufacturer Baker vouchsafes: "To the Far East, on the trade routes of the world, Baker's marine paints ensure protection, appearance and economy."

Manufacturer Charlie says simply: "Charlie's marine paints are used in over two million tons of shipping."

These manufacturers are to be commended for their modesty. Certainly we can find no extravagant claims here. In fact, they do not claim anything except that they manufacture paint.

Let us examine some of the reasons we have encountered for some purchasers to specify or buy a particular brand of paint: 1. The price is cheaper per gallon; 2. The weight is greater per gallon; 3. Cosmetic appeal of the container or advertising; 4. He used to go to sea with the salesman, who has always been a nice chap; 5. The particular paint happens to be stocked by the shipyard doing the dry-docking; 6. He tried some on his garage once and it held up well; 7. The advertisement says, "It was originally invented by a sea captain"; 8. The manufacturer made up a paint schedule for the ships so the mate will get the right stock numbers and colors on his requisition; 9. The manufacturer ships his paints in the owner's ships.

Not a single cogent reason except the last one, and even here we will probably find that the freight revenue received is completely disproportionate to the cost of the paint purchased.

Materials Consumption

Table 9 gives a comparison of the cost of materials purchased for five similar ships during 1959. The variation between vessels of 81 per cent in the cost of deck materials and 345 per cent in the cost of engine materials suggests that this account is really a surge chamber for the basic maintenance account.

A review of another company's fleet of fifteen ships revealed the annual total cost of materials for the low ship was $35,500 and for the high ship was $98,500, a variation of 357 per cent compared with the 66 per cent variation in these five ships—certainly further evidence that this is not a clearly defined and controlled account.

TABLE 9.   DOLLARS PER YEAR

	DECK	ENGINE	TOTAL
	C 15,940	A 4,980	A 27,850
	B 16,040	D 12,360	B 29,680
	A 22,870	B 13,650	C 38,100
	D 26,880	E 17,290	D 39,230
	E 28,850	C 22,170	E 46,140
Average	22,100	14,100	36,200
Variation	81%	345%	66%

NOTE: Stewards' materials not included as dollar amount is not significant. Spare parts not included as they are charged to maintenance.

Conclusions and Recommendations

The purchasing for and supply of materials to ships operating in irregular trades constitute an extremely difficult task. Short port time, irregular schedules and diversions to other ports all contribute to making the purchasing agent's life a nightmare of variables and changes. In liner trades, however, these handicaps disappear when regularity and supervision become available.

New materials, particularly steel coatings, are usually greeted with no lack of prejudice in the marine industry. This is especially true if the product's name is something spelled backward. When new materials are given tests on board ship, there often results something less than complete follow-up. People tend to examine the newly installed materials with great interest, then send the ship to sea and forget about it.

Some of the materials used today show a unique lack of imagination. Many owners paint their ships a color known as haze gray, which was developed by the Navy to make the ship harder to see. How better could collision be invited?

The marine industry has a bigger stake in solving the problems of corrosion than any other industry, yet few marine maintenance engineers belong to the Society of Corrosion Engineers, read their literature or attend their meetings.

On a 35,000-ton bulk carrier, as much as 60 per cent of the cost of maintenance materials furnished to the crew is spent on paint and coatings used to combat corrosion.

The majority of these paints and coatings used on ships today are purchased with little if any knowledge of the product's composition either quantitatively or qualitatively. Additionally, many other materials of maintenance and replacement are often purchased on the basis of price, reciprocity or expediency with no quality or service life evaluation.

A sound program should be developed for the analysis, testing and evaluation of all paints, coatings, systems of cathodic protection and any other means of combating corrosion available. The practice of continuing open-minded materials evaluation is to be recommended. Ideally, this should be done as a team effort between the operating and maintenance departments.

Due to inborn marine conservatism, improved materials and techniques usually appear years earlier ashore than on ships. Safety, however, is also a necessary factor in air and space travel, and in these industries engineers have adopted four-dimensional thinking. They consistently solve material and other problems by refusing to dream about better mousetraps and spend their time looking for alternative ways to kill the mice.

Requests for materials to be used aboard ship for preservation, maintenance or replacement purposes should be approved by the person normally responsible for the maintenance function, who should specify and be responsible for the make, type, quality and quantity of all maintenance materials purchased. The purchasing department should be responsible for the purchase of the specified material at the lowest possible price and for its timely delivery to the vessel at the time and place specified.

Material costs are traditionally broken down in total by deck, engine and steward department. This relates back to the days when the heads of these departments stayed on the same vessel for many years and were thus held personally responsible for their own group's material costs. The value of this practice today is doubtful.

Generally the materials of maintenance are not codified for consumption or cost control purposes. The true sources of the expenses cannot, therefore, be easily identified. A ship's material costs (the so-called stores account) are in reality an appendage to and a surge chamber for the maintenance account. All materials used in the maintenance of vessels should be charged to the applicable "cause code" in the regular maintenance account.

CHAPTER SIX

Insurance

I N 1953 Thomas J. White wrote an interesting paper (Bibliog. 13), which in clear language for the layman gives us a well-distilled glimpse at the history and evolution of marine insurance.

Ancient History

"Marine insurance reputedly had its commercial beginnings in the practices of the merchants of the island of Rhodes nearly 900 years before the birth of Christ. In those days it was known as bottomry and General Average was a well-known principle. It was even drafted into the official language of the Rhodian law which provided that, 'If in order to lighten a ship merchandise is thrown overboard, that which has been given for all shall be replaced by the contribution of all.'

"Bottomry bonds in the early days had one important feature which appeals to every assured who has had to contest a claim with his underwriters. In the ancient bottomry contracts, the underwriter paid out the money at the start of the voyage and received it back, with a premium, if the vessel arrived safely. Needless to say, there were in those days dishonest shipowners who preferred to sink a poor vessel in return for the underwriter's gold. Demosthenes has recorded that one Hegeatratus was discovered cutting a hole in his ship's bottom, whereupon he threw himself overboard and was drowned. Such a practice has not disappeared to this day, to the consternation of the underwriters, as witness the rash of vessels which sank after World War I. No fewer than forty-one vessels were lost in early 1921. In fine weather they suddenly sprung unexpected leaks utterly beyond the control of the pumps. The crews, of course, were invariably saved. The vessels struck mines in the most unlikely places and ran ashore in a most incredible fashion."

Recent History

"It seems conceded that the advent of true marine insurance came with the Lombards who settled in London in the twelfth century, bringing with them the long experience in dealing in money which was at a more advanced stage in Italy at that time than elsewhere. The Hanseatic League with its maritime code provided a stability to commerce that had been missing since the days of the Roman Empire, and maritime commerce began to flourish. However, when Edward Lloyd opened his coffeehouse on Tower Street, London, in 1687, the hey-day of marine insurance began. Due to its strategic location in the city, the masters of vessels putting into London adopted the habit of dropping in at Lloyd's. As the coffeehouse became more and more the recognized meeting place of men of the sea, it also developed into a center for the marine insurance business. Masters, who might also be owners of their ships, recognized that at Lloyd's they would likely find merchants willing to insure both ship and cargo. Through the years, in its transition from coffeehouse to the recognized center of the insurance world, the practice of marine insurance was developed to its well-formulated methods of today."

Why Insure?

We will probably get few arguments in stating the premise that some forms of endeavor are safer than others. Lying abed is safer than walking, and walking is safer than running. Experience demonstrates without question that we suffer more fortuitous tragedies when swimming, jumping or flying than when standing still. We know that a horse and wagon cannot disappear on land but a ship can disappear in minutes at sea. In other words, there are certain perils peculiar to the sea which do not exist on land. For this reason, land endeavors seem primarily concerned with the risk of liability, while sea endeavors seem more concerned with the risk of great material losses in addition to the risk of great liabilities arising out of collision.

While the early Greek philosophers debated which was the primary element of the universe, whether water, air, fire or earth, voyagers by sea learned that each of these elements boded danger for them. Their vessels were exposed to being swamped every time air gathered as a great wind raising boisterous seas and blowing them toward a lee shore. There, jagged rocks of earth were ever ready to breach their vessels as were strands to grip and hold them fast. Water would engulf them to destruction but was seldom equal to quenching a devouring fire. We might sum up the manifold advantages of insuring against marine perils by saying that it: Substitutes certainty for uncertainty; eliminates the paralyzing effect of worry and fear; distributes losses to the ultimate consumer; results in the cheapest distribution of losses; serves as a basis of credit.

The basic function of insurance is the elimination of risk by the substitution of certainty for uncertainty. The certainty which is furnished by insurance is the premium cost, which is a definite cost accepted by the assured in exchange for an indeterminate, uncertain threat to his financial position.

Self-Insure?

It has been said that over the years the cost to insurers of particular classes of claims shows little variation in the proportion they bear to the bulk premium received. It has been estimated that total losses take about a quarter, and about half of the premiums go for ordinary particular average damage claims. General average, salvage, sue and labor charges and collision liability account for the balance.

For example, let us take the owner of a single ship worth $5,000,000. If he insured the ship at a hull rate of 1 per cent and could maintain this rate, he would pay underwriters only $1,000,000 in premiums during the ship's 20 years of life. On the other hand, if he annually funded this premium in a 4 per cent annuity, it would take him 41 years to achieve a fund balance that would compensate him for a total loss.

Alternatively, if the owner estimated that only one-quarter of his premium was used by underwriters in general to pay total loss claims, then, at a 1 per cent rate, he might conclude that his chances of a total loss were only 1 in 400. On this basis, he might fund only one-quarter per cent annually, in which case it would take him 72 years to achieve a fund balance that would compensate him for a total loss.

This all sounds very good, but if the ship sinks in the first year of operation, then the shipowner has lost his $5,000,000, his credit and, last but not least, the principal tool of his business. If he is a Henry Ford or a Giannini, then he can start from scratch and will possibly own another ship in several years. If not, then he can sell chestnuts outside Grand Central Station.

Whether or not a company is self-insured, the risks are real and the expense of insurance must be considered a real cost. Self-insurers usually set up an insurance reserve on their books and charge each voyage with a proportionate premium to create a reserve. Obviously, self-insurance can be practiced only by the largest of operators with sound backing or otherwise bankruptcy would be a daily possibility.

Property insurance has become a part of the very fabric of our civilization and culture and is considered virtually indispensable to our present economic system. Today, no sensible businessman would consider for a moment foregoing the benefits of its protection. Property insurance has done much to encourage the growth of industry by lifting the important burden of risk from those who would pioneer in new ventures. For example, in the aviation, space, electronics and other rapidly developing industries, there are sufficient uncertainties already without the additional risk of destruction of property by fire or similar perils. In practically every form of business enterprise, sound insurance protection has been an encouragement to the investment of capital in the face of these additional risks.

Insurance appears to be a keystone of our modern credit system under which most ships, planes, homes, cars and other substantial purchases are financed today. When property subject to destruction by fire or other hazards forms the basis for a loan, few bankers today will extend credit unless insurance is carried as protection for the loan.

An Illustration

An example of how a series of marine perils can inexplicably attack a single owner in rapid succession is rather well illustrated in Francis E. Hyde's excellent history (Bibliog. 14) of the Alfred Holt Company, *Blue Funnel:*

"On the night of 4 October 1875, the *Hector* was lost on a reef outside Amoy Harbour. The sinking of this vessel, worth £36,000 to the Company, was the first total loss which had been sustained. It was to be quickly followed by others; the *Orestes* was sunk off Galle on 7 March 1876, and the *Sarpedon,* through collision with a Belgian steamer, the *Julia David*, off Ushant on 4 September. The immediate loss to the Company by these disasters was estimated at £120,000 with a total loss of well over a quarter of a million pounds. Serious as this was, the adverse effects of such events might have been mitigated had the remaining ships in the fleet been able to avoid any further accidents. To the alarm of the Managers, however, a succession of collisions, groundings and breakdowns of machinery occurred; voyages were unnecessarily delayed; valuable cargoes were lost, a falling revenue had to be set against a mounting cost for repairs and compensation. The *Ulysses* in her first year of sailing went ashore in the Red Sea and had to return to England 'causing a heavy loss on the voyage'. In the following year she lost her propeller and was run ashore again, this time near Singapore. Then came an epidemic of broken shafts. Apart from that in the *Ulysses,* which was nearly lost altogether, the *Antenor,* the *Ajax* and the *Agamemnon* had to receive repairs, the latter ship having two shafts fitted in a single voyage. These mishaps were followed by the *Menelaus* coming into collision and sinking a pilot boat in the Mersey. There was then a period comparatively free from accidents until 1880 but, in the year, the *Achilles* with a cargo of new tea ran aground at Hankow and had 'to pay a large sum to the China Navigation Company's steamer *Shanghai* for towage.' The new *Hector* was almost as unlucky as the old; in 1881 she was in collision with a foreign steamer in the Channel, a misfortune which involved the Company in lengthy and costly litigation; and in 1884, she touched a reef near Singapore 'under circumstances which did not seem to justify the Managers in retaining the services of her master.' The *Telemachus* with a valuable cargo of tobacco aboard broke down off Finisterre and incurred a heavy towage charge. Finally, to round off this most unhappy chapter of accidents the *Teucer,* filled to capacity with Sumatra tobacco, was lost off Ushant in 1885."

Insurance Premiums

Marine insurance premium rates are determined by a variety of factors, which are constantly changing. The most significant factors seem to be the:

Ship's age and type	Reputation of the owner
Ship's value	Loss experience of the owner
Ship's intended trade	Ability of the broker
Number of ships in owner's fleet	Insurance market

Even though all these values are constantly changing both quantitatively and qualitatively, most of them are really beyond the owner's control. He can, however, do everything within his power to enhance his reputation, select the most able broker and reduce his casualties.

Protection and Indemnity Insurance

Protection and indemnity insurance (referred to as P & I insurance) is an insurance coverage obtained by the shipowner against losses for which he may possibly become legally liable as a result of certain risks and happenings, among which are the following: loss of life, injury and illness; deviation for landing injured or ill seamen; customs, immigration or other fines or penalties; damage to docks, buoys, bridges, etc.; damage to vessel's cargo or cargo contamination; cost of cleaning up oil spills; costs and charges of legal services.

Tables 10, 11 and 12 show an analysis of the illness and injuries suffered by the crews of five ships over a 27-month period. These are only the cases which resulted in hospitalization or repatriation home.

Any conclusions to be drawn from this tabulation should possibly be made by someone trained in medicine, but even the layman cannot help but notice that (1) gastrointestinal complaints are the most numerous and expensive and (2) the type of injuries seem minor in nature and are principally confined to the extremities.

Inasmuch as the deductible feature of this particular insurance is $700 per case, it will immediately be seen that a substantial portion of the costs of these 69 claims was borne by the owner. Of the $43,570 cost of these claims:

Insurer's pay	$ 8,430 or 20 per cent
Owner's pay	$35,140 or 80 per cent

Additionally, several cases of surge damage to docked vessels were encountered during the subject period, and insurers are expected to contribute some $6,500 to these claims. The whole picture, then, for this period would seem to be:

Insurer's pay	$15,000	
Owner's pay	$35,000	$35,000
Total losses	$50,000	
Premiums paid		$163,000
Owner's total cost		$198,000
Cost per ship per year		$ 17,600

TABLE 10.   ANALYSIS OF ILLNESS AND INJURIES
Five European Crews—27-Month Period

	NO. OF CASES	COST
Venereal Disease	3	$ 710
Back Strain	1	730
Ear Complaints	2	780
Skin Disease	2	960
Heart Disease	2	1,100
Varicose Veins	2	1,300
Tonsillitis	4	1,740
Sinusitis	2	1,870
Illness (Unclassified)	8	3,850
Illness (Other)*	6	5,090
Injuries**	16	9,520
Gastrointestinal	21	15,000
	69	$42,650
Not Yet Paid		920
		$43,570

*Abscesses, Kidney Stones, Miscellaneous.   **See Table 11.

TABLE 11.   LIST OF INJURIES WHICH RESULTED IN CLAIMS
Five European Crews—27-Month Period

Alleged leg injury	Car accident	Injured ankle
Assault	Fall off ladder	Injured knee (2)
Back strain	Fractured jaw	Injury to finger
Beating by crew	Hernia	Injury to forearm
	Injury (unclassified) (2)	Steam burn

TABLE 12.   ILLNESS AND INJURIES
Claims Cost Analysis By Cost Group

$	NO. OF CASES	$ TOTAL OF CLAIMS
0–99	6	240
100–199	3	497
200–299	2	500
300–399	19	6,633
400–499	6	2,555
500–599	2	1,136
600–699	8	5,224
700–799	6	4,451
800–899	5	4,317
900–999	6	5,669
1,000–1,499	3	3,737
1,500–1,999	2	2,539
2,000–3,000	0	
3,000–4,000	1	3,640
	69	

Hull and Machinery Insurance

Hull and machinery insurance is placed on the vessel to insure against loss of, or damage to, the vessel, her equipment and stores arising from certain risks and perils of the sea, among which are the following: heavy weather, sinking and stranding; collision, striking rocks or sunken obstructions; fire, bursting of boilers, breakage of shafts; accidents to the vessel in loading or discharging cargo; accidents to the vessel in bunkering or in taking on fuel; explosions on shipboard or elsewhere causing damage to the vessel; damage resulting from latent defects in machinery or hull; negligence of the master, charterers, repairers, crew, engineers or pilots.

With the exception of sinking, stranding, collision and fire, this type of insurance coverage is usually subject to a so-called "franchise," which is a value of damage (usually $4,850) which must be sustained in order to permit a valid claim to be made under the policy.

Tables 13 and 14 show an analysis of casualties encountered by five vessels over a period of about two and a half years. The casualties are analyzed by number and by cumulative cost within various cause categories and cost groups. It can be seen that this type of analysis lends itself to a review of the effect of the selected franchise value.

TABLE 13. CASUALTY ANALYSIS BY NUMBER OF CASUALTIES

| | | COLLISION WITH | | | |
	STRANDING	SHIP	OBJECT	DOCK	BOILER	TOTAL
$ Cost						
0–5,000	21	1	1	5	2	30
5–10,000	3		2	1		6
10–15,000	3	1	1			5
15–20,000	2					2
20–25,000	2		1	1		4
25–30,000					1	1
30–40,000	2					2
40–50,000						
Total Number	33	2	5	7	3	50

TABLE 14. CASUALTY ANALYSIS BY COST GROUP

| | | COLLISION WITH | | | |
	STRANDING	SHIP	OBJECT	DOCK	BOILER	TOTAL
$ Cost						
0–5,000	1,489	1,068	1,700	10,015	8,316	22,588
5–10,000	16,172		15,160	9,300		40,632
10–15,000	53,823	14,036	14,952			72,811
15–20,000	35,942					35,942
20–25,000	48,280		24,000	25,000		97,280
25–30,000					27,180	27,180
30–40,000	78,883					78,883
40–50,000						
Total Cost	234,589	15,104	55,812	44,315	35,496	375,316

Conclusions and Recommendations

The root function of marine insurance is the substitution of certainty for uncertainty. The vast capital requirements of shipowning and the protection demanded by lending institutions in the face of marine risks make insurance against catastrophic loss mandatory. Self-insurance of large fleets, funded or not, can be accomplished only by owners with exceptional backing or vast cash reserves.

Except for the extinction of sea monsters, the magnitude and variety of the perils of the sea have not diminished since time began. Physical damage to ships takes many varied forms. This damage usually *results* from the proximity of the property to one of the elements such as earth, water or fire. But the damage is often really *caused,* the stage set, by human failure. The *remote* causes must be found and eliminated in order to prevent a recurrence.

The basic nature of the ship, as a piece of floating property exposed to sea perils, has not really changed since the first canoe was built. Today's ship is infinitely more complex and theoretically safer, but Archimedes' first screw bilge pump of 200 B.C. would have saved the *Andrea Doria* from sinking as well as a Roman galley.

Each country appears to investigate accidents with a different degree of thoroughness. Some countries appear to have no investigative machinery at all, while others seem quite interested in determining the true causes of accidents and the extent of human failure involved.

It is possible that a substantial amount of seamen's ills, together with the resulting cost and time lost therefrom, could be prevented or minimized if a doctor and dentist were carried on board, either continuously or intermittently. Collaterally, it is possible that such a practice would invite additional legal liability. Alternatively, it is possible to tighten up on pre-employment physical examinations. The examinations given to seamen who are going to sea for a year do not compare in thoroughness with those given to employees in other industries who contemplate foreign service under frontier-like conditions.

The principal effort which the owner can make toward lowering his insurance costs is in reducing his casualties, and this can be done most effectively by employing only the best officers obtainable. An old ship with a well-trained crew is infinitely safer than a new ship manned by people merely assembled at random. Effective safety flows principally from training and conditioning, not from legislation.

There is much to be said for a shipowner to retain the best insurance broker obtainable. An able broker's knowledge of the insurance market and counsel in investigation and settlement of claims are invaluable.

The state of the art of damage control and fire fighting on most merchant ships is elementary at best. This can easily be remedied by providing all officers and petty officers with a proper damage control and fire-fighting school. Such instruction should take at least a month and be of the same quality as the schools operated by the U.S. Navy, which give practical experience in damage control and fire fighting. It would be in both the owner's and the underwriter's interest to jointly sponsor the creation of such a school.

Management should promptly receive a brief, uncamouflaged report of every vessel casualty or accident. The report should contain the:

Vessel's name	Cost of repairs
Accident description	Cost of time lost
Location	Proximate cause(s)
Time lost	Remote cause(s)

These data can easily be accumulated in brief form for quarterly analysis. The annual total of such data will highlight the soft spots in the personnel, safety or maintenance programs.

Films on safety topics and related educational subjects are available. They should be shown to the crew along with their diet of entertainment movies. Safety bulletins, safety posters and similar propaganda are available. They should be used to maximum advantage.

CHAPTER SEVEN

Definition

I N THE beginning of this study we had some rather high expectations when we grandly said, "Hopefully, we may identify those elusive criteria of smart economical ship operation which have heretofore escaped definition." As humans have done for several thousand years, we have been hoping to stumble over some profound precept, some common denominator, some basic law that without much work could be applied to our efforts to tell us whether we have been doing things efficiently and whether we have been getting what we paid for.

Heaps and Piles

Now it was this very wonderment about value and application and quantity that used to be so frustrating to our relatives who lived in rent-free caves instead of heavily mortgaged ranch houses. It is reported that the quantity of three was the highest specific number that brother cave man perceived or used. Three squirrels could be considered a fair trade for one rabbit, three spearheads for one deer. What they did in the matter of large or small deer probably created the first panel of three arbitrators. In those days, quantities beyond the number three were reportedly referred to as "a heap" or "a pile."

In his animal-like environment, prehistoric man was of course severely handicapped in his pursuit of a means to understand and factorize his "piles" of squirrels and "heaps" of fish. Firstly, he had no measuring concept to apply to the objects or happenings that he couldn't define anyway. There is good reason to believe that somewhere along the line man has discovered that definition and measurement are inseparable. For example, can we define an object too unimportant to measure? Seemingly not, for we have already started to measure its importance in just stating the question. And to measure undefined objects or happenings would merely be measuring for measuring's sake.

In Chapter I we set out to examine and define the nature of our operating costs. In so doing, we hoped to find the fundamental reasons for all the things we do and for the way we do them. Our basic questions have really been: Why do we employ large crews which must be paid, housed and fed? Why do we perform mountains of maintenance and buy tons of materials? Why do we insure against every imaginable peril at not inconsiderable cost?

We have been going through the process of defining what we do and trying to determine whether we know why we do it. In a general sense, there is some reason to doubt whether we know why we do many things except from inertia and custom. The "Preservation of Fiction" by intentional design plays as great a part in governing our actions today as it did in medieval times.

A Bag of Cats

People have always been understandably reluctant to give away their military or commercial secrets. This is purely a matter of self-preservation. Additionally, the egregious part of man continuously acts as armor on his Achillean heel to prevent him from revealing his problems to those who would take advantage of him. The result of these natural instincts together with the evolutionary nature of maritime development over centuries of time have effectively kept our problems in the dark. The scholar who would speak was without experience data. The manager who had the data was silenced by the gag of self-preservation. The few brave souls who have ventured to speak or write on our fundamental problems can be counted on our fingers.

The press and commercial magazines of the past century no doubt contain a collective record, but by and large it resembles a galaxy of bits and pieces. As the maritime world has simultaneously shrunk in size and increased in complexity, the natural result has been the creation of an army of specialists who dare not write on the broad aspects of ship management and consequently deprive themselves of the depth of field that brings full focus.

Listening to this army of specialists, each telling us what his little speciality can do for us, is not unlike being bombarded by ads on television. Quite naturally, vested interest has done its Spartan best to keep the cats in the bag.

Captain Sullivan Defines and Measures

According to our research, it was not until 1921 that the articulate Captain D. J. Sullivan, in his discussion of a paper (Bibliog. 15) titled *How Can American Ships Compete Successfully With Foreign Ships?,* let several of the cats out of the bag and gave refreshing definition to the problems of ship management that existed in 1921, many of which still exist today. Captain Sullivan said in part:

"I happen to be a master of a ship under the American flag, a graduate engineer who first started to sea as an engineer."

"From the time that I assumed the command of that ship, a year and a half ago, until the present day, there has been less than $4,000 expended in repairs for maintenance."

"We have reduced the fuel consumption on that ship from 42 tons a day to 28. We took the ship with an average speed for the transatlantic voyage of 9.4 and brought it up to 10.8."

". . . the cost of my crew today is $3,007.50 a month, or $2,300 less than the cost of the crew on a Shipping Board vessel on May 1. The cost of subsistence for the crew is 50 cents a day per man, from master to mess boy."

". . . and on board my ship we insist on at least 99 per cent of the time being devoted to the work of making the repairs and allow the repair gang only 1 per cent of the time to shoot craps."

"When that ship is steaming at sea, she is immediately forgotten. She is turned over to the master from the time she clears the custom house in New York and leaves the dock, and the office force throw their hands up and say, 'Thank God, she's gone.' "

"One of the important considerations in American steamship operations is the analysis of its cost."

". . . and without going into detail, I will say if we can get 100 per cent honest men in the steamship business, I think we could reduce the cost of operation 25 per cent."

Apparently, Captain Sullivan's rare candor resulted in an invitation for him to write a paper (Bibliog. 16) for the 1922 SNAME convention, for the records show that on November 9, 1922, this engineer, turned sea captain, presented a paper entitled, *Efficiency in the Operation of Steamships.* Although a relatively short paper, the title was intriguing by virtue of its rarity. While Captain Sullivan's remarks should be read in total to be fully appreciated, the following statements made by him seem to indicate his ability to define fundamental problems and objectives:

"When these men [American Clipper Masters] won the supremacy of merchant shipping for American vessels it was said of them in 1860 by a critic of the merchant marine of another nation: 'We have no masters who can match the masters of American vessels, and until we do, and allow them full control of our vessels, we cannot compete successfully.' "

". . . and with the perfection of systems of communication the status of the master and officers was reduced to practically that of a high priced office boy obeying orders issued from ashore by those who were intoxicated by high freight rates and large profits."

"Much could be written about the subject of insurance—all classes—but it would not influence the prevailing opinion of those who should know the subject fairly well. Any discussion on this subject can be summed up by saying that when loss and damage are high the rate is high and when loss and damage are low the rate is low."

"The question of subsistence, while not very large in total cost, is most important in having satisfied personnel afloat, and sufficient care should be exercised to see that food is properly prepared and made appetizing instead of the all too common practice of serving improperly prepared and unpalatable food."

"The master should be furnished with complete cost data so that he can remedy high cost over which he has control and show the owner the excessive cost over which he has no control."

"To accomplish this result there should be closer relations between the executives of companies and the masters of their vessels. Masters should be selected for their efficiency and given absolute authority over the operation of their vessels."

It appears that Captain Sullivan knew more than a little about the important business of plugging cash leaks. And it seems doubtful that he ran an unhappy ship; of his seven officers, six were college graduates, and it is highly unlikely that they were unreasonable buckoes.

It would seem unnecessary to take up further space by dwelling on Captain Sullivan's observations—he has already paralleled many of our findings and recommendations.

No Crutch to Lean On

Since the first cave man used a log to float himself across a river, the marine industry has been gathering practices and procedures based on yesterday's experience. Empiricism has been the rule, precedent the guide. Custom is a major force to be reckoned with even when systems are demonstrably weak, for the difficulties of retraining and re-educating, to say nothing of the problem of developing better systems, frequently operate to hinder improvement.

As a comparison it is rather interesting to observe the air transportation industry, which has developed to its present state, except for the early promotional stages, with only one generation of managers. Joseph L. Nicholson, in his comprehensive text, *Air Transportation*

Management (Bibliog. 17), makes these observations on management and efficiency:

"A sound thrifty management, whether in an airline, a railroad, or a manufacturing company, generally secures a substantial part of its net results from the many leaks stopped and the many little increases in efficiency gained."

"It must be kept in mind that any single yardstick of management is apt to be meaningless whether it be used for airlines, corner grocery stores, or any other businesses. One airline may benefit from better routes while a second line gains from a longer average passenger haul. Furthermore, even poor management can make a profit on a cost-plus contract or in a sellers' market. But good management exploits its advantages and tries to lessen its disadvantages."

"A criterion of good airline management is its ability to promote its advantages and to lessen its disadvantages."

"The best method of comparing one airline with another is a comparison of the total operating expense per ton-mile. However, even ton-mile costs are subject to constant change."

"In airline operation, the emphasis on standards of efficiency varies from airline to airline. One company may base its standard on the quality of its passenger service; another, on low operating cost. To the economist, the yardstick is a composite one, reflected in the record of profitable operation."

"There are other evidences of the uniqueness of airline management. With a very few exceptions, have its principal officers had any major business experience outside of aviation. The air carriers have drawn heavily on pilot personnel in recruiting for executive positions. The importance of technology in air transportation has resulted in an emphasis on technical knowledge rather than business ability."

In *Technical Aspects of Air Transport Management* (Bibliog. 18), R. Dixon Speas offers further interesting definitions and precepts on aircraft maintenance:

"Maintenance of aircraft is not exceeded in importance by any phase of operation as to effect upon reliability, reputation, and economy of the airline."

"It is often difficult to disassociate items related to airworthiness and assign varying degrees of importance with respect to operational reliability. It is much safer, easier, and more practical to have only one standard of maintenance—the highest practical—without regard to whether the item is related to air safety."

"The primary factor in determining airline maintenance quality is found in the quality of personnel."

"All maintenance irregularities and difficulties can be convincingly attributed to poor engineering design, faulty construction, or improper operating techniques. For example, a heater failure can be caused by (1) deficient design, (2) material failure, or (3) improper operation."

He has this to say on cost control:

"An airline recently endeavored to budget its operating costs by over-all departments. The responsibility and authority for enforcement of the budgeting did not extend below the offices of the vice-presidents. As such, the budgeting became a cost-following function, not a cost-control aid."

"Three different types of cost breakdowns are usual in airline accounting procedures. One method is to segregate costs according to departmental responsibilities. This breakdown is valuable in making inter-airline and intra-airline comparisons if adjustments are made according to assigned responsibilities."

"A second type of cost breakdown is with regard to function. The third breakdown distributes costs under the two categories of direct flying costs and indirect flying costs."

The foregoing definitions of efficiency and maintenance criteria are most interesting, but let us pass over them for the moment and examine Mr. Speas' observations on cost control.

It is apparent that, while the airlines break down their costs in three different dimensions in order to measure controllability better and to budget function, in the steamship business we use only a single cost breakdown. Our method consists of examining our costs by departmental responsibility, which is only one of the measurements used in the air industry. Let us try to reconstruct the circumstances that have created our pattern in order to understand better its possible advantages or disadvantages.

The Voyage Account

Historically, it has become more or less traditional to measure the success or failure of a ship on a completed voyage basis. Indeed, we have only to turn back to the nineteenth century to find that the return of a ship from its voyage used to be a very uncertain thing. *Lloyd's List,* covering the period from 1793 to 1829, reveals an annual average of 557 shipwrecks, over 800 occurring in that last year alone, when more than 2,000 seamen perished. With the termination date of the voyage being such a problematical thing, it is understandable that early shipowners or managers wished to keep the books open until each individual *adventure* was completed. In those times, each voyage was indeed a separate project in itself, requiring the shipping of a new crew, careening the hull for repairs and caulking, outfitting, and taking aboard sufficient food and water for the intended voyage. In effect, the ship was reconstituted and fully restored to its original state in condition, equipage and men. A package account of the so-called voyage or venture would seem appropriate.

This accounting of the venture exists to this day, where its most prominent use is probably in the building and construction industry.

Its purest use in the ocean shipping business is by the time charterer who is using someone else's ship to prosecute a given voyage or series of voyages. Here is lump sum accounting at its finest, in which the ships' operating costs never vary from minute to minute or month to month . . . for the charterer.

The Cumulative Account

The owner, however, is not so fortunate in the matter of grappling with the many variables of operating cost, which, for the present at least, can be integrated only after a long period of time by the profit and loss statement. We do not careen our ships for caulking each voyage or hire a new crew. We do not refit and completely restore the ship to its original state or condition, thus providing a sacrosanct cut-off date to measure the cost of the last voyage or period.

All we can do is estimate, reserve, hope and then adjust our next estimate. Regardless of the skill we use in this estimating and adjusting, the end result is merely a more accurate forecast of expenses. This, of course, is of vital necessity in keeping operating capital at a minimum, but it accomplishes no cost control function. This is a "cost following" function.

The defect in this procedure is that the department head who is the forecaster is commended and rewarded for his accuracy, not for his efficiency. His lump sum forecasts can unintentionally hide great waste and excessive cost . . . for the spotlight is not on imagination, innovation or economy but on making the forecast come true.

Let us look at some of the possible reasons why we have shackled ourselves with the single dimension of departmental measurement.

Account Defined

Webster gives us our choice of definitions for the word "account," and the relevant ones seem to be:

1. The series of items under one heading in a company's ledger.
2. A statement and explanation, as of one's discharge of responsibilities.
3. To serve as explanation.
4. A statement in general of reasons, causes, grounds, etc.
5. A statement of facts; narrative, report.

In our industry we use definitions 1 and 2 together. Historically, since Mr. Marconi obtained his patent in 1896, shipowners have found reason to employ an engineer superintendent, a port steward, a purchasing agent, a paymaster and a claims agent. The accounts then, as we use them, are "the series of items under one heading in the company's ledger" which relate to the expenditures made by these individuals. This sense of responsibility is a valuable thing and should not be tampered with unnecessarily. But it suggests that the origin of these things might be in the days when there were neat little fences around the duties of each department head. These were the days of Captain Sullivan and before. These were the days when a bath was taken from a bucket and there was no overtime pay. Repair by replacement was virtually unknown and the crew accomplished most or all of the onboard repairs. The engineer superintendent was principally concerned with the repairs in dry dock.

It is suggested that surprise repairs were something of a rarity in the days of sail. Certainly those masters could accurately estimate the marine growth that would attach to their bottoms after X days in this or that tropical port. And the life expectancy of this or that make of canvas and cordage must have been known to the nearest month by even the sailors.

But what a shock it must have been to the sailing-ship owner when he bought his first steamer and found he had rid himself of uncertainty from the winds at the price of uncertainty in the repair costs. Previously, faced with surprises limited in extent to, say, 10 per cent in such matters as material costs, he now found himself living with a Hydra with a roving decimal point. His reaction was probably to build a fence around his engineer superintendent to determine how much money this man spent, and to hold him responsible for it.

Little imagination is required to envision the shipowner building additional fences around his paymaster and purchasing agent to determine how much of his money they were spending. But these fences provided only useless checks on honesty and frugality, both unmeasurable qualities.

Reliable estimates based on experience show that current annual average operating costs of 35,000 DWT bulk carriers or tankers of other than American flag are as follows, give or take $100 a day.

*COST CATEGORY	$	%
Wages and all benefits	$129,800	30.7%
Subsistence	23,700	5.6
Repairs	102,100	24.2
Stores and supplies	30,800	7.3
Insurance, all (and deductibles)	122,900	29.1
**Miscellaneous	13,200	3.1
TOTAL	$422,500	100.0%

*Account names generally in use today.
**Agency, communications, etc.

Figure 1 shows the picture we get by grouping our expenses together in this manner by departmental responsibilities.

The First Dimension

This is the dimension in which we do our record-keeping today. It is based on account parameters which relate to the contracting feature in the mechanics of buying services and materials. These account groups are in reality the names of people who approve expenditures for propriety and cost. The accounts are not definitive but are general and overlapping. For example, Wages merely means the annual total of all the payrolls, regardless of whether the labor was used for operating, safety, cargo handling or maintenance of the ship. This method allows cost control only on an individual item basis and precludes costing anything but the total effort.

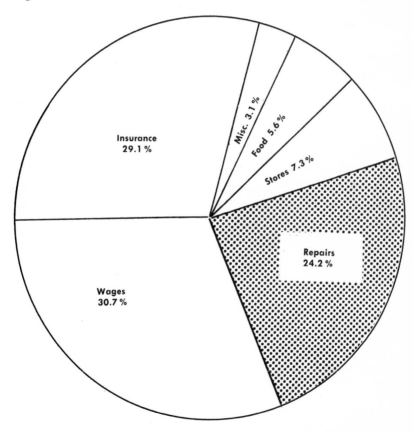

Figure 1.

The Second Dimension

This is a new dimension to contemplate, and it requires a bit of effort because it is foreign to our conditioning.

In Table 2, we saw that 38.5% of total wage and related food costs is directly attributable to the performance of maintenance work on board a ship and the remaining 61.5% is related to keeping watch and operating duties. Now, if food is charged to the men who eat it and the men are charged to the true root function they perform, we will get quite a different picture of the source of our principal expenses.

We also know that some 80% of our materials purchased is used in maintenance. In this dimension, they are charged to their source.

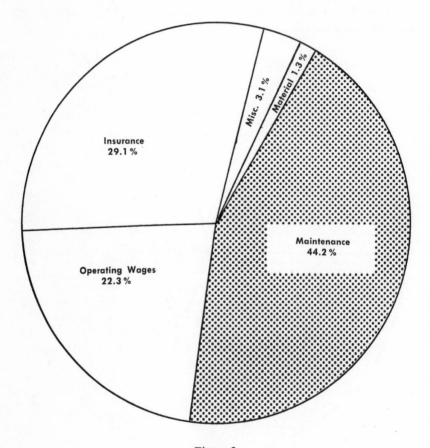

Figure 2.

The Third Dimension

This dimension is based on the consideration that marine insurance premiums are payable in advance, and once paid are uncontrollably gone. Inasmuch as insurance is a requirement of financing, we have here removed it from controllable operating costs and considered it a capital cost. Actually, if a $5,000,000 ship could be so built to be accident-free for an additional $2,000,000, we would certainly consider this extra capital investment in lieu of insurance.

This approach tends to purify our problem of fixed payments to others and confines it to the controllable expenses of operating and maintaining the ship. Figure 3 now represents about $300,000.

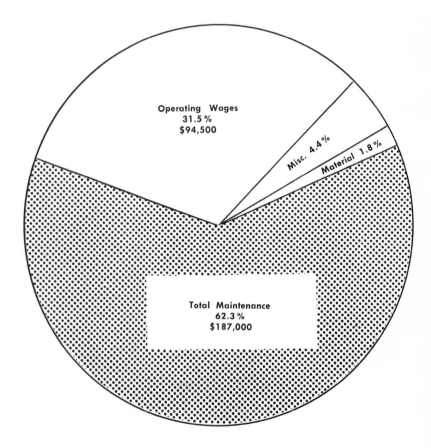

Figure 3.

The Fourth Dimension

A recent detailed analysis of ten ships operated by three different owners revealed the following revenue time lost during a year from various causes:

Scheduled dry-docking and related maintenance   72 days
Maintenance failure   26 days
Other causes*   28 days

This means that 98 days or 9.8 days per ship per year were lost through scheduled maintenance and maintenance failure. Assessing an arbitrary but reasonable cost of $3,000 per day, we find that further hidden maintenance losses cost another $30,000 a year.

When overtime is used to save time in the course of routine or emergency maintenance, its cost is charged to maintenance. When

---

* Collisions, strandings, latent defects, diversions and other fortuitous occurrences.

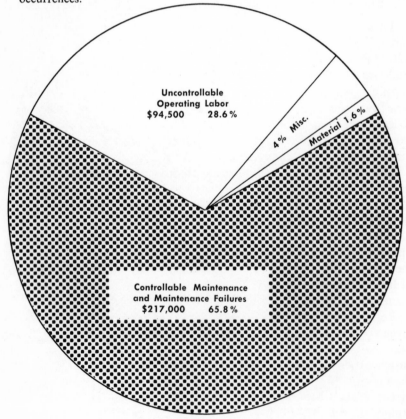

Figure 4.

overtime is not used, the time so lost is unidentifiable, as it merely becomes a part of the over-all profit or loss picture.

In this fourth dimension, we have charged the "Maintenance Function" with the real cost of the real time that was really used.

Preserving the Fiction

Some recent comparative operating costs for a C-2 type of freighter under different flags appeared in the *New York Times* on August 29, 1960. The costs that were given have been converted here to annual amounts for more significant comparison.

ANNUAL OPERATING COSTS $

	Wages	Other	Total
Norway	113,500	175,900	289,400
Great Britain	128,800	178,500	307,300
Germany	109,500	198,500	308,000
United States	450,400	246,700	697,100

These estimates are interesting, but they must be read with some care. For example, the fact that German "other" costs are some $20,000 higher than Norwegian and British does not reflect a higher standard of maintenance or wasteful spending, but probably indicates certain operating costs which are borne by the governments of the other two countries. Similarly, the higher United States' "other" costs reflect the higher insurance costs of a United States' flag ship and the existing *ad valorem* restrictions imposed against the purchasing of materials and maintenance services abroad.

The principal thing that these estimates again demonstrate is the propensity of the marine industry for (1) looking at operating costs in total, (2) mistaking the money symbol of the word "wages" as a function and (3) ignoring the root sources of its expenses.

There is some reason to believe that the apparently uncompetitive operating costs of United States' flag vessels cannot be explained away merely on the basis of higher wages, or even less on the vague grounds of higher safety standards. The fact that these higher wages are being "consumed" on board ship is a result, not a cause.

Regardless of a ship's flag or the crew's nationality, two of the largest operating costs are nondiscriminatory, and are likely to remain so—fuel and stevedoring. Additionally, port charges, communication expenses and overhead are usually determined by factors other than nationality. As to capital cost, foreign-built ships can be registered in the United States provided they compete only in foreign trade. Again, the quality, speed and safety of the ship will remain a function of imagination and ability, not of origin, nationality or legislation.

Just because a dog is born in a stable, it does not follow that he should be called a horse.

The only real difference in the running costs of two similar ships under different flags is in the cost of the functions that take place on board the ship: the operating function and the maintenance function.

For a comparison with the previous function analysis (Table 2) made of European wage costs, Table 15 represents a similar factorization of the same costs on a comparable United States' flag vessel. It is worthy of note that the relative cost of these two functions varies by only 2 per cent when comparing the American and European crew.

TABLE 15. WAGE BREAKDOWN (U. S. FLAG)
By Groups
Wages and Food Cost Related to Service Performed

	MONTHLY BASE WAGES, 55% OVERTIME, VACATION, PENSION. WELFARE	FOOD	TOTAL	%
Keeping Watch				
Master, 3 Mates, Radio Operator, 5 Able Seamen	$11,056	2,060	$13,116	31.5
Chief, 3 Watch Engineers, 3 Firemen, 3 Oilers	9,643	2,060	11,703	28.0
			24,819	59.5
Maintenance				
Bosun, 4 Maintenance Men, 3 Ordinary Seamen, Pumpman, Able Seaman	7,099	2,060	9,159	21.8
1st Engineer, Electrician, 2 Maintenance Men, 2 Wipers, Pumpman	6,346	1,448	7,794	18.7
			16,953	40.5
Feeding				
Steward, 2 Cooks, Galleyman, 5 Messmen	5,769			
Total (46 Men)	$39,913		$41,772	

NOTE: Food charged to each group at rate of $1.33 per man-day and weighted with proportionate amount of stewards' department wages plus their food.

Now, using the same costs for outside maintenance and materials as for the European ship and bypassing all the intermediate steps, we have synthesized the American picture of controllability in Figure 5. Additionally, 9.8 days of lost revenue time due to planned maintenance and maintenance failures have been used at a cost of $5,000 a day. The controllable annual maintenance cost of $387,000 adds up in 20 years to the tidy sum of $7,774,000 or 77 per cent of the (American building) cost of the ship.

Fortune magazine for September, 1937 (p. 206), gives a major shipbuilder's estimate of this maritime endowment to be 75 per cent. The closeness of a 24-year-old estimate and today's actual figures suggests that the time has come to let you draw your own conclusions.

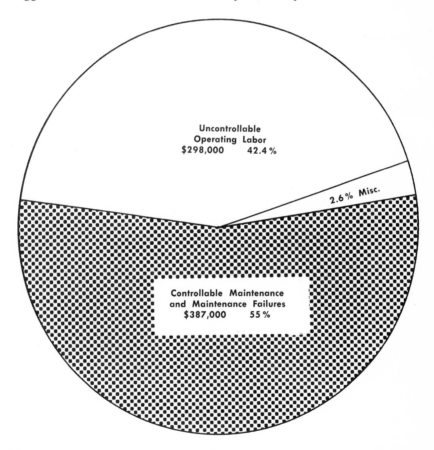

Figure 5.

CHAPTER EIGHT

Measurement

T O THE man who has spent a lifetime observing our fascinating industry, it may seem that we have succeeded only in making the obvious more clear. Even if this be so, we are not too disappointed, for, at least, we have not made our problems less clear, and the definition of our problems is the root purpose of this study. Albert Einstein once said, "The mere formulation of a problem is far more often essential than its solution, which may be merely a matter of mathematical or experimental skill."

Clarifying the Obvious

As we have constructed our many definitions, we have done some measuring along the way. It would be a mistake to assume that all these measurements have import and significance, *ipso facto*. Some of them were made out of curiosity, and some out of curiosity as to what it would cost to make them. It should not be forgotten that any measurement is costly to make and must therefore return at least its own cost to justify its existence. However, the ingredients of the measurements we have made are all taken from routine papers we handle every day. If the right numbers can be caused to separate themselves automatically, then of course our measurements will be almost free.

And despite the hard work and thinking and time required to take our measurements, they are still not corrected to any standard; nor are any performance measurements taken in the marine industry in particular or in business in general. We do not correct to 60° Fahrenheit, to a standard barometer, to place, time, people or circumstances.

Automate What?

Recalling that when the first oil well was brought in, 96 per cent of all hard labor was performed by man and today that same amount is performed by machine, we must realize that in the short space of one lifetime, animal-like toil has been abolished. We are, in time, heading toward almost complete automation, and this includes at least semi-automation of ship operations. We already have machines that can remember, analyze and think logically. Our scientists and engineers have not yet produced machines that can perform the functions of creative imagination, and one aspect of this thought might be "less power to them."

Certainly there are some tasks, and there probably always will be, that require special judgment or imagination to perform. Additionally, there are tasks which, for the present at least, are awkward and cumbersome to automate.

One of the first questions which comes to mind is: What are we trying to automate? We cannot just say we wish to automate labor, for this is meaningless. What we are really trying to automate are functions, and to automate them they must be identified and measured. The justifiable capital cost of an automatic device is revealed only *after* determining from experience the present worth of the cost of the non-automated function.

Eliminating the necessity to take star sights, to write some approximate numbers in a log book, or to clean fuel oil burners is one form of automation which is worth while only if the end result is a reduction in the number of people required. If not, then it may merely be a further contribution to the already critical state of seagoing boredom. Many people would still rather "sling fat" at a noble reciprocating engine than stand under a ventilator feeling sorry for themselves.

Dr. Porsche's contribution to automation was not on the Volkswagen assembly line. It was on the battlefield of "built-in maintenance load." To eliminate the necessity for maintenance of a component, or better yet to eliminate the component, is perhaps the purest form of automation, although the word symbols we use seem to effectively camouflage this simple fact.

From our study of operating costs today, it would appear that we are not quite ready to prepare for the automated ship described in Chapter I. This is because we would be trying to automate the unknown if we cannot put a time and cost value on each function performed by the crew, the ship, the maintenance staff, and so forth. There is reason to believe the semi-automated ship will not arrive in 1970 unless we prepare for it.

Feedback

The absence of reliable cost breakdown by function and root cause has a serious dampening effect on the efforts of those who design even our conventional new ships. Look for a moment at the arms' length relationship between the people who design ships and those who operate them. The designers regularly complain that they never see the results of their designs or hear of operating or maintenance troubles. Admittedly, when the shipowner takes his troubles back to the designer, he often gets the same reception as a boy bringing home a bad report card. This is because he usually takes bits and pieces back to the designer. And bits and pieces usually look suspiciously like unrepresentative sampling. On the other hand, how many naval architects and marine engineers who were really responsible for the basic design concepts remain on board the ship to observe the results of their decisions after the trial trip?

So, as in the days of Magellan, the argument goes on over whether the helm should be located in the front or the rear of the pilothouse instead of wondering if something else would not be better than a helm or why a helm is needed at all. The designer cannot find out how much the operating function costs or how much money is spent on boiler maintenance or underwater corrosion. It is, therefore, impossible for him to convert these values to a present worth basis for comparison with the installed cost of an automated feature or an improved but more expensive material. This lack of communication between the user and the designer has a strong tendency to seduce the designer into dusting off the old plans of another ship, instead of being able to use his creative imagination to build a better ship requiring less operating labor and having a lower "built-in maintenance load."

The Time Factor

The element of time in our measuring and reporting is an interesting one to consider. It offers great opportunity for contemplation and reflection. The moving of goods over the water is a form of energy utilization, and to measure it properly we must measure weight, distance and time. If we do not realistically measure any one of these three factors we will get a distorted picture of the energy expended. If we ignore time, we will only get an instantaneous picture of a force, not energy. In practice, the weight and distance can be measured with reasonable accuracy using existing methods. But it requires special judgment to decide over what period of time we measure to insure that we will obtain representative results that can be used as tools.

Certainly a lifetime or a decade is too long to wait for answers. We may not even be here when they arrive. On the other hand, it would seem quite crisp and efficient to see our financial and operating statistics roll out continuously on a ticker tape or to be able to read them instantaneously at any moment as on a torsion meter. But this would not be representative of any period of time and would not weld together our many highs and lows.

The solar year would seem to have some advantages as a cut-off date for our reports and statistics. Everyone remembers what year it is and that the earth makes one revolution around the sun annually. If we were in the meat or wool business, this period, by the grace of God, coincides exactly with the periodicity of the birth of our lambs; and the government requires us to tote up all our expenses and revenues once each solar year in order to calculate the taxes due them. This would seem to be a compelling reason to adopt the 365-day accounting and reporting period . . . if our product is crops.

The shipbuilder might well get better results from an accounting period of 240 days, while the builder of dams and bridges might like a period of 630 days. We see here the possibility that many of us have become mesmerized by the tax collector into thinking that we must cut all our patterns to fit his 365-inch bolt of cloth. From an administrative standpoint, it seems quite reasonable that the tax collec-tor must slam his iron gate on everyone's fingers at the same time. But this point in time is by its very nature arbitrary and can, therefore, have meaning to only a few.

The emotional effects of this tax barrier are worth considering too. It carries a connotation of the judgment day of all things, which is not true. Similarly, January implies snow, July recalls firecrackers, and October means pumpkins. These things have come to be emotional symbols as well as marks on a calendar. If we let them, like any emotional symbol written or spoken, they will make us do things we do not necessarily intend to do.

The use of arbitrary cut-off dates can introduce substantial error and delusion in our measurements, for the accurate reduction of dynamic operations to static figures is not an easy thing to do. There is some reason to believe that the solar year and the lunar month might have more in common with astronomy than with business or engineer-ing. Additionally, the human memory has been found somewhat in-adequate for periods of time longer than thirty days. As with all animals, punishment or reward must closely follow the act to be of much value.

Life is Just a Bowl of Measurements

Recently, while pondering Samuel Butler's quip that "life is the art of drawing sufficient conclusions from insufficient premises," we got to wondering why all the premises have to be so insufficient. This thought led us to theorize that perhaps all the premises we observe and collect are merely more measurements.

From the moment we arise in the morning we start to measure—the time, the weather, the one inch of toothpaste on the brush. This measuring goes on ceaselessly all day long with people measuring anything and everything and also each other. It apparently continues until sleep again overtakes the conscious mind. It is easy to think of thousands of measurements we take very day, but we fail to recognize them as such because somewhere along the line someone has synthesized a special noise or word in French, English, Latin or German to describe this particular action and enrich the language.

This enrichment of the language has a strong tendency to breed the language of the specialist, which is irrespective of nationality. In addition to Portuguese, we now have insurancese, engineerese, accountingese and legalese. Yet, if all these specialities could be stripped of their attractive trappings, we might find some common denominators. And Neanderthal man, with his unenriched noises, might view the unfrocking with the observation that "all these fellows are doing is measuring; they're just measuring different things."

This common denominator of measurement, if it be so, gets more interesting the more we think about it. Wondering if anyone else had thought about it, we wandered into a large library recently, and found that other people had indeed thought about it. We found hundreds of books about what people "know" about measuring everything from alpha particles to zebra stripes.

But what we were really looking for was some knowledge of the distance between what we already know and what we could know. We found only one book about what people "don't know" about measurement. It was the end of our search and it was delightful. The name of it is *Measurement: Definitions and Theories* (Bibliog. 19), and it was edited by two gentlemen named C. West Churchman and Philburn Ratoosh at the University of California. It is a small book and it costs $8.00. It is underpriced.

Measurements and Decisions

Paul Kircher, in *Measurement: Definitions and Theories* (Bibliog. 19), suggests dividing the basic structure of the business measurement process into the following key elements so that each may be studied with more precision and the relationships between them more clearly seen. Kircher's proposed elements are: defining the objective; determination of relevant factors; selection of key aspects; choice of measuring method and unit; application of the measuring unit; analysis of the measurements; evaluating the measurement.

This factoring of the measurement process is a natural and an excellent way of outlining or planning any problem solution. It could otherwise be stated as follows: while suspending all judgment—define the total real problem; identify all key aspects; assemble the maximum number of known solutions; construct new solutions by recombination and synthesis; analyze the new total possibilities; evaluate the obviously best alternatives.

Here again, we see that the identification of key aspects is a cornerstone of any problem solution whether the problem be measurement or otherwise. There is some reason to suspect, however, that nearly all problems can be reduced to a measurement problem. The "what" in most problems is usually apparent or given, whether it be weight, time, ability, affection or what have you. It is the need to quantify that creates the problem.

Kircher gives us an example of the importance of defining "Key Aspects" from general accounting practice. He says:

"An example can be drawn from accounting. Various types of assets and liabilities are measured in order to obtain information concerning the revenue and expense flows, and the financial position of the firm. These indicate the degree of attainment of the profit-making objectives of the business.

"The illustration from accounting is especially interesting since accountants have deliberately chosen to restrict their activities to those measurements which they believe *can be made within a certain standard of accuracy*. This means that certain other items, vital to the well-being of the firm, are resolutely omitted."

In explanation of the "vague" characteristics of business. Kircher gives us a clearly distilled definition:

"As in all logical analysis, there are many aspects of business which rest on undefinable terms or unprovable propositions. In the past these have been so numerous and so important that business has been characterized as an art. There have been few precepts of general significance—each new problem the manager encountered was seen as being a brand-new one, at least in some respects, 'Business is an experiment'."

Standards

It is not unusual in our industry to have disputes and even less unusual to find that the disagreement is over some form of measurement. Measurement of ability, degree of negligence, reasonableness, weight, speed and, yes, even distance. It is not uncommon to find a shipowner and charterer in disagreement over the precise speed of a vessel, in spite of the fact that we do not have instruments today that can accurately and reliably measure the speed through the water. Their argument is over something that cannot (yet) be accurately measured, and their own figures are based on "the apparent speed over ground that the ship didn't go over."

In evaluating the measurements we take in the marine environment, it should be remembered that we seldom adjust them to agreed standards of temperature, time, place, people or other variant conditions. This lack of adjustment, and in some cases nonadjustment, flowing from absence of standards is probably what excites the "yes, but" function in many of the readers of our measurements and reports. C. West Churchman clearly sums up the three "levels" of adjusting measurements to standards (Bibliog. 20):

"Thus, we see three 'levels' of standardization of data. The first tries to restrict itself to data reports that are virtually certain to remain invariant with time and place so that zero adjustment is required. This level minimizes the cost of adjustment, but the data themselves have little precision and, consequently, little value where refined distinctions are needed.

"The second level consists of rejecting data not collected under standard conditions. The method of adjustment is simple, but the waste of information may be considerable.

"The third level consists of adjusting data to standards by means of 'laws' that enable one to say: if report R_1 was made at time T_1 in circumstances Z_1 by a person having properties W_{11}, W_{12}, etc., then report R_0 would have been made at time T_0 in circumstance Z_0 by a person having properties, W_{01}, W_{02}, etc. The 'standards' are specified in terms of circumstances, observer, and observer actions."

Why Measure?

In a broad exploration into the meaning of measurement, Churchman's paper (Bibliog. 20) clearly identifies the four key areas of the measuring environment. In his candid, if not too optimistic summary, he states:

"The decision making problems of any of the aspects of measurements are enormously difficult, and even an approximation to their solution still escapes us. Everything that has been said here about measurements is applicable to a broader class called 'information' and 'data.' A rather significant portion of our resources is devoted to generating and processing data. However, it is apparent that no one knows how the data should be expressed (the decision problem of data *language* is unsolved), what data are needed (the decision problem of data *specification* is unsolved), how the data are to be used in various contexts (the decision problem of *standardization* is unsolved), and how the data are to be evaluated (the decision problem of *accuracy* and *control* is unsolved)."

On the subject of accuracy and control, Churchman states: "The decision problem of accuracy, therefore, has not been adequately solved, except possibly for some industrial process where there is repetition of data and cost functions can be obtained."

Now here is a suggestion in which we can take heart. Certainly we have a repetition of data, and cost functions can be obtained. Perhaps we are not presently obtaining these key cost functions, but they are certainly available, just for the taking.

There seems to be no lack of labor-saving tools available for the back-breaking job of handling and processing great quantities of data and information. As long as seventy years ago, punched card accounting machines were being used to classify, file, collate, add, subtract, multiply, divide, total, reproduce, print and post data punched into cards. In that year of 1890, it can be recalled that coal was still the principal fuel and that many sails were still being used. There is some indication here that we have spanned the era from sail to nuclear power without yet having (1) defined our objectives, (2) selected the key aspects, (3) chosen the measuring methods and units or (4) started to measure.

There is good reason to believe that we can and must solve the problems of measurement that confront us today, for we have an infinitely greater task than our counterparts of 1890. As the social, political and economic environment has become more complex, and our job of holding the reins has become more difficult, the need for competent guidance from realistic measurements has become even greater. The manager who once concerned himself only with bookkeeping and a few broad measurements must now tackle labor questions, technical problems and national, state and local regulations of encyclopedic proportions. He must have significant reports and meaningful measurements in order to guide himself and his associates on the current and long-term aspects of these and other related subjects.

We can all remember the days when each department seemed to live inside a walled city. The accountants kept a steely eyed watch on the cash box and the engineers jealously guarded their dusty rolls of blueprints. Each specialist minded his own business and expected other departments to mind theirs; but as companies grew and became more complex, these walls have progressively come down. They have had to, for in today's world no specialist or department can possibly exist by itself in a vacuum. Everyone has benefited tremendously from today's freer give and take, which is in effect the creation of a system of communication where none existed before. We can now communicate our measurements to each other.

More and more we recognize that our measurements are only a means to an end and never an end in themselves. We now realize clearly that our measurements become useful only when they are constructively presented, correctly interpreted and finally translated into action. These heavy responsibilities clearly indicate the need for the ultimate degree in teamwork between all the members of the management team.

Afterword

We have narrowed down the focus of our discussion from a broad exploration of ship management and operating costs to the problems of measuring our performance, and it is at this point that we must stop and you must begin. If we have succeeded in our purpose, you should now see yourself and your role in our business in a somewhat different light. Although you may now see problems of which you have not been aware, you should also see that we have strengths and powers that we have minimized. By using them we can better control the course of our affairs.

Basically, what we have tried to accomplish here is to illustrate a way of thinking more deeply about the problems of our business, a way that uses not only the simple tools of analysis but the more important techniques of recombination and synthesis. We must now select those parts which appear to have import and significance, discarding or modifying those that do not. In other words, we must perform that most difficult of all human tasks, to think for ourselves.

If, of all that has been said here, you have found some useful concepts, some new understanding, some way to improve our performance or its measurement, then the three thousand hours we have spent in writing this book and the three hours you have spent in reading it will be amply rewarding for both of us.

Bibliography

Bibliography

1. *Fabulous Admirals,* by Geoffrey Lowis. Putnam and Company, Ltd., London, 1957.

2. *A Case Study of Innovation,* by Dr. Elting E. Morison. Engineering and Science Magazine, April, 1950, published at the California Institute of Technology.

3. *Atomic Industrial Forum Report R-31,* Speech by Representative Herbert C. Bonner, pp. 153-54, Atomic Industrial Forum, New York, 1960.

4. *Some Observations Regarding Merchant Marine Personnel,* by Professor Em. H. L. Seward. Transactions SNAME, Volume 47, 1939.

5. *Human Problems in Marine Engineering,* by C. C. Pounder. Transactions SNAME, Volume 67, 1959.

6. *Sans Taste, Sans Everything,* Courtesy Time; copyright Time Inc., 1959.

7. *History of American Steam Navigation,* by John H. Morrison. Stephen Daye Press, New York.

8. *Legal Liabilities of Shipowners as Affected by the SS* Pennsylvania *Case,* by James L. Adams. SNAME Northern California Section, February, 1959.

9. *Ship Maintenance and Repair,* by Panel 0-29 of Ship Technical Operations Committee. Transactions SNAME, 1959.

10. *The Corrosion of Cargo Ships and Its Prevention,* by H. J. Adams and J. C. Hudson. Transactions I. Mar. E., November, 1956.

11. *Some Aspects of the Application of Planned Maintenance to Marine Engineering,* by W. H. Falconer. Transactions I. Mar. E., February, 1957.

12. *Survival At Sea,* by G. W. R. Nicholl. Adlard Coles Ltd., Southampton, 1960.

13. *The Inside Story of Marine Insurance,* by Thomas J. White. The Log, October, 1953.

14. *Blue Funnel,* by F. E. Hyde. Liverpool University Press, Liverpool, 1957.

15. *How Can American Ships Compete Successfully With Foreign Ships?* Discussion by Captain D. J. Sullivan. Transactions SNAME, Volume 29, 1921.

16. *Efficiency In The Operation of Steamships,* by Captain D. J. Sullivan. Transactions SNAME, Volume 30, 1922.

17. *Air Transportation Management,* by Joseph L. Nicholson. John Wiley & Sons, Inc., New York, 1951.

18. *Technical Aspects of Air Transport Management,* by R. Dixon Speas. McGraw-Hill Book Company, Inc., New York, 1955.

19. *Measurement: Definitions and Theories,* Chapter III, *Measurements and Managerial Decisions* by Paul Kircher. John Wiley and Sons, Inc., New York, 1959.

20. *Measurement: Definitions and Theories,* Chapter IV, *Why Measure?,* by C. West Churchman. John Wiley and Sons, Inc., New York, 1959.

ADDITIONAL RECOMMENDED READING THAT WILL PROVIDE INSIGHT INTO THE SOLUTION OF MANY PROBLEMS IN SHIP MANAGEMENT

21. *Some Shipowners' Problems,* by Rupert Munton. Transactions North East Coast Institution of Engineers and Shipbuilders, Volume 75, 1959.

22. *These Splendid Ships,* by David Divine. Frederick Muller Ltd., London, 1960.

23. *Principles of Engineering Economy,* by Eugene L. Grant. The Ronald Press, New York, 1950.

24. *Some Aspects of Automation in Ships,* by G. Kaudern. Paper presented to the Royal Institution of Naval Architects in Gothenburg on September 7, 1961.

25. *Shipowners' Responsibility with Reference to Seaworthiness of Ships and Brief Comments on the Early History of Same,* by B. E. Meurk. Paper presented to the New York Metropolitan Section SNAME on April 25, 1947.

26. *The Folklore of Management,* by Clarence Randall. Little, Brown & Co., New York, 1961.

27. *Objective Accounting,* by Carl F. Braun. C. F. Braun & Co., Alhambra, California, 1953.

28. *The Marine Engineer and the Common Life,* Presidential Address of C. C. Pounder before the Institute of Marine Engineers, London, October 3, 1961.

29. *Precautions and Pitfalls in the Operation of the Modern Marine Steam Power Plants,* by Dr. Lester M. Goldsmith. An address to the Greater New York Safety Council, New York, March 25, 1947.

30. *Applied Imagination,* by Alex F. Osborn. Charles Scribner's Sons, New York, 1957.

The author is grateful for permission to quote from publications listed in this Bibliography.

Index

Index

Index